How to Catch a
Flying Saucer

How to Catch a Flying Saucer

James M. Deem
Illustrated by True Kelley

Houghton Mifflin Company
Boston   1991

For David and Chloe,
twin skywatchers

Library of Congress Cataloging-in-Publication Data

Deem, James M.
  How to catch a flying saucer / James Deem ; illustrated by True Kelley.
    p. cm.
  Includes bibliographical references.
  Summary: Discusses the characteristics of UFOs with descriptions of sightings and tells how to become a UFOlogist.
  ISBN 0-395-51958-6
  1. Unidentified flying objects—Juvenile literature.
[1. Unidentified flying objects.] I. Kelley, True, ill.
II. Title.
TL789.D43   1991   90-4931
001.9′42—dc20   CIP
                      AC

Printed in the United States of America

CRW 10 9 8 7 6 5 4 3 2 1

Contents

Introduction

Have you ever stared at the sky on a cloudless night? The moon is a bright circle, the stars shine like diamonds, and the sky glows with possibility. If you are like many people, you are not just watching the sky in wonder. You are looking for any sign of movement. A passing jet, perhaps. A falling star.

Mostly you are waiting to see a UFO.

And you are not alone.

Over the last twenty years, various polls of the American public have shown that almost half of the people who are aware of UFOs believe that they are real. What's more, many people believe that they've seen a UFO.

But *believing* in UFOs is very different from *knowing* the facts about them. Some people are all too ready to accept the existence of extraterrestrial UFOs, while others feel that UFOs can't exist at all. Whatever you think, you will need to know the facts.

You may have some questions about UFOs. Do they come from outer space? Are they secret military weapons? Or are they imaginary?

Although it isn't wise to assume that all or even any UFOs come from outer space, many of the stories in this book may lead you to conclude that at least some do. Other stories may convince you that UFOs are secret military aircraft. Still others may help you realize that people are sometimes mistaken when they claim to see UFOs.

Whatever you believe now or end up believing, I hope the information encourages you to explore the subject of UFOs to discover facts, not just opinions. The stories I've included are all real stories. They have been reported by people who saw something quite unusual and took the time to describe their experiences. I've found them in the United States and England, in libraries and in UFO research centers. I have not invented anything; I've simply written down the facts as I found them. In some cases, I have made up names for unidentified people or changed the names of individuals in order to protect their privacy.

I have not retold many of the famous UFO stories. Instead, I've tried to present less well-known cases, which are often more exciting. Many of these stories may have you thinking that wonderful UFOs are being seen each day. The sad truth, though, is that fewer UFOs have been reported in recent years. Is it because the craze has passed and people have become tired of imagining extraterrestrials and their airborne vehicles? Or is it because UFOs come in waves and we're merely in the lull before another surge in sightings?

The job of proving what UFOs are falls to a group of people known as UFOlogists. Although the name may sound very official, anyone can call himself or herself a UFOlogist. Some are college professors and librarians, some are astronomers or other scientists. But you can't take a degree in UFOlogy at college. Some UFOlogists are interested in proving that UFOs involve visitations by beings from other planets, while others want to disprove that idea. Two UFOlogists investigating the same case may have quite different purposes in mind. Do you want to be a UFOlogist? This book will help you learn how.

Because I think knowing the truth about UFOs is more important than believing in them, I ask you to report any encounter you might have. If you would like to share it, please write to me: James M. Deem, c/o Houghton Mifflin Company, Two Park Street, Boston, Massachusetts 02108.

Whatever you do, as you scan the heavens for unidentified flying objects, keep your feet planted firmly on the ground and get ready to research any discoveries you make.

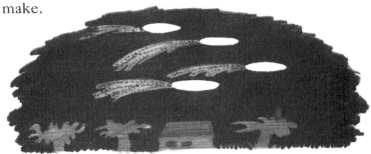

PART I
The ABCs of UFOs

1. The UFO Possibility

On January 31, 1978, three young boys were "bootskat-ing" on the ice-covered playing field of the Montvale Memorial Elementary School in Montvale, New Jersey. Eddie Hargrove, his brother Michael, and their friend John Cummings watched as a flying object approached and hovered overhead.

Since it remained stationary for almost five minutes, the boys got a good look at the object. It was square with rounded corners and appeared to have a dome on top. It had a yellow light at each corner and a light underneath, which cast a red beam that stopped just short of the ground.

Eddie, Michael, and John quickly realized that they were seeing something strange. As the flying object moved away, they became frightened and ran to the dugout by the school's baseball diamond. By then, the object had disappeared. Before they could discuss what had happened, they noticed what looked like a man in a yellow jogging suit across the road from the field. Michael thought it was a neighbor who frequently jogged in the evening.

"Mr. Johnson," Michael called to the man, "did you see that UFO?"

Immediately the man turned toward the boys, and Michael gasped. The man was not Mr. Johnson. His head was shaped oddly, and had a crease down the forehead; he looked more like a hawk than a man. Then, before he could answer, ten other creatures, all in yellow jogging suits, joined him. Each one was bald and had large, dark, square places where his eyes should have been; their skin was light yellow. They walked stiffly, like Nazi soldiers, according to John. "Have you heard of Hitler's army?" John later asked a UFOlogist who interviewed him. "You know how they walked, kind of stiff, with their arms straight? Well, that's . . . how they looked."

The appearance of the "joggers" wasn't the only strange thing that happened after the hovering object disappeared. All three boys noticed that the surroundings had grown eerily silent. They also detected a pungent sulfur smell.

Mustering their courage, they left the dugout to get a better look at the yellow-suited creatures. Some were walking back and forth, while others headed down a nearby road. Then the boys noticed another figure — a woman, they believed.

The woman, who was wearing a short dress, had no facial features. As Eddie said, she just had skin on her face. She walked down the road to a low fence, where she sat down. She pointed at the three boys, as if to signal them, then raised her arm skyward. Eddie, Michael, and John looked up and saw the squarish object flying toward them. The woman stood up and began to walk away. A police car drove toward her, but as it approached, she disappeared. After it has passed the spot where she had been, the boys saw her reappear and continue walking.

As she got farther away, something even stranger happened. "Parts of her," the three boys later reported, "kept going away — disappearing — and coming back again." Finally the woman walked through the rear wall of a building and disappeared completely.

So did the creatures in the yellow suits, but the boys had concentrated so much on observing the woman that they did not see what had happened to the men. Now everything was normal again — almost.

The boys hurried to John's house and banged on the door. John's brother, Hilton, looked out the window to see what was the matter. He saw the boys at the door, but he also saw a spinning object in the sky. It had yellow and red lights exactly where the three other boys had seen them earlier. Hilton let his brother and his friends in. After a few minutes' discussion, they decided to telephone the police. As it turned out, no other UFO reports had been made that night. But the boys didn't doubt for a moment what they had seen.

By now you might be wondering if the boys really saw a UFO. They said that they saw something in the sky. Could it have been an airplane? After all, they lived on the flight path for Newark Airport.

You might also wonder if the boys saw the yellow-clad UFOccupants. Perhaps they were so frightened by the flying object that they turned ordinary people into aliens.

And what about the strange woman? Why was she pointing at the sky, and did she really disappear? Maybe she was a ghost. Or maybe she was just a tired woman walking home from work who happened to stretch her arm a moment.

Were the boys playing a prank? Or were they so scared by a passing plane that they imagined a spooky UFO tale? Were they trying to get some attention? Or could they have been telling the truth?

Three UFO investigators, Budd Hopkins, Ted Bloecher, and Patrick Huyghe, decided to study the case. Before you discover what they found out, take the following quiz to see how well grounded your UFO knowledge is.

The Eddie, Michael, and John Quiz

Decide which of the following statements are true, based on the story you read.

1. Eddie, Michael, and John said that they definitely saw a UFO.
2. Eddie, Michael, and John saw a UFO.
3. Eddie, Michael, and John saw creatures from outer space.
4. The yellow-suited creatures came from the flying object.
5. The strange woman was a companion of the yellow-suited creatures.
6. The woman also came from the flying object.
7. The first yellow-suited creature was John's neighbor, Mr. Johnson.
8. Since no one else reported seeing a UFO that night, Eddie, Michael, and John couldn't have seen one.
9. Without a doubt, the UFO came from outer space.
10. There is no proof that Eddie, Michael, and John saw a UFO.

The answers to this quiz may surprise you. Only the first and last statements are true. The boys said they saw an unidentified flying object, but that doesn't prove that they were telling the truth. Perhaps it was an alien spaceship; perhaps it was just a helicopter. Unfortunately, no proof of their encounter existed other than their own testimony. All of the other statements are either unprovable (2–6) or definitely false (7–9).

What did the investigation uncover?

Hopkins, Bloecher, and Huyghe called the boys' parents and arranged to investigate the encounter. On February 5, five days after the initial sighting, they arrived in Montvale. The men inspected the playing field and surrounding area. They also interviewed each boy privately.

The investigators had two questions in mind: Were the boys lying, or had they seen something? If they had seen something, could it be explained by normal circumstances?

In the course of their questioning, the men tried to trick the boys into admitting that they hadn't really seen a UFO or any strange creatures. They questioned the boys about *Star Trek*, *Star Wars*, and *Close Encounters of the Third Kind*. But they learned from Eddie and Michael's father that his sons had never been interested in science fiction. The boys stuck to their story. As Budd Hopkins wrote in his report, "It became clear to all three of us by the end of the day that the boys were not perpetrating a hoax."

If the boys has actually seen a UFO, the men wanted to know whether it was something ordinary (like an airplane or a helicopter) that had caused the boys to jump to conclusions about every person they next encountered. When the New York Air Traffic Control Center and Newark Airport reported that no flying object had been picked up on radar in the vicinity of Montvale that evening, the investigators decided to center their inquiry on the creatures.

Could they have been joggers?

Officer Pelsang of the Montvale Police Department reported that he had been on duty that evening and had seen no group of joggers. In fact, he had never seen more than two people jogging together in Montvale and "never after dark. No one jogs after dark. They'd have to be crazy." Officer Pelsang was certain that he would have noticed a large group of joggers.

If they were not joggers, could the creatures have been employees of the Department of Public Works (DPW)?

The headquarters of the DPW were opposite the school's playing field and near where the boys first saw the yellow-suited aliens. The three men discovered that the DPW workers wore yellow uniforms in bad weather. However, Lewis Bradley of the DPW stated that all workers had gone home at 4:30 P.M. on the day in question and that none were wearing yellow uniforms that day.

The investigators were persistent in their questioning. Could another group of workers have been there that day?

"Look," Mr. Bradley said impatiently, "there are only six men who work here, and I'm the boss. I just finished handing in their time sheets."

As for the female creature, no one else had seen her. That left Hopkins, Bloecher, and Huyghe with no way to prove or disprove the boys' encounter.

Did the boys see a UFO? The investigators concluded that the boys' reports should not be ignored. They agreed with Officer Pelsang, who said, "Twelve-year-old boys don't call the police unless they're really upset about something." The boys must have seen something real that night. However, no matter what the investigators wanted to believe, they could not prove that anything had happened. As they wrote in their final report, "The story is interesting but, alas, the amount of value from a case of this kind . . . is doubtful."

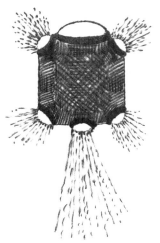

2. UFO Mythology

In many ways, Eddie, Michael, and John's encounter is like hundreds of others that have been reported throughout history. The story is tantalizing, the witnesses are sincere, but no conclusive evidence is found. This lack of proof has caused a number of UFO myths to obscure the facts.

Myth #1: UFOs come from outer space.

An unidentified flying object is simply something in the sky that no one recognizes or understands. You could be playing with a Frisbee in a park and toss it from behind some bushes. A girl walking by who didn't recognize the Frisbee might think — for a moment, anyway — that she's just seen a UFO. When she realizes that the object is really a Frisbee, the UFO becomes an IFO: an identified flying object.

Suppose you are walking down a road one night and you see some mysterious lights overhead. You're sure you have seen a UFO. However, when you check further, you discover that the lights were simply those of a commercial jetliner. Of course, you might also find that no airplanes were reported flying in the vicinity that night.

The truth is that most UFOs definitely don't come from outer space. After some study, about 90 percent of the UFOs reported turn out to be IFOs: stars, planets, comets, meteors, lightning, advertising planes, clouds, or even birds! As for the UFOs that remain unidentified, no one knows where they come from or what they are. Some may indeed come from outer space. Others may be secret military weapons or aircraft, like the stealth bomber. Some may contain travelers from a future time. They might also be completely imaginary. *But no one knows.*

UFOlogists who claim that real UFOs come from outer space base their ideas on the belief that other intelligent beings must exist in our galaxy. After all, there are perhaps 200 billion stars similar to our sun in our galaxy alone. Like our sun, these stars may have planets revolving around them. If intelligent life could develop on Earth, it could also develop on some of these other planets. It stands to reason that creatures from another

24

planet would be curious about life in our galaxy. Therefore, people who report seeing UFOs might be seeing spaceships and aliens from other worlds.

UFOlogists who do not believe that UFOs originate in outer space suspect that people make mistakes in reporting what they see. In fact, they claim that these reports are not to be trusted. So many people have made up stories or produced fake photographs of UFOs that it must all be a joke. Finally, these critics claim, if UFOs really existed, we would have good, clear photographs taken by more than one person at the same time from different angles, which would definitely prove a UFO's existence. And if UFOs really come from outer space, why haven't the space travelers simply introduced themselves to humans? Since they haven't done that, they just don't exist.

Despite what both sides *believe*, no one has enough facts to say anything for certain. But many interesting ideas exist.

UFOlogist Jacques Vallee believes that UFOs may come from other dimensions than space and that we Earthlings are just not smart enough to understand them yet. He points out that in many ways the stories people tell after encounters with UFOs and UFOccupants are very similar to the stories people have told throughout the centuries about elves, fairies, leprechauns, and other supernatural creatures.

In contrast, author Manfred Cassirer believes that UFOs are similar to ghosts. Like ghosts, most UFOs are seen at night. Like ghosts, some UFOs are reported to disappear. In fact, as more and more people have reported seeing UFOs, fewer people have reported seeing ghosts. Could UFOs, Cassirer wonders, be a new type of ghost?

Who is right, Vallee or Cassirer? Each man *believes* that he is, but no one knows for sure. Still, many UFOlogists are interested in both ideas.

Myth #2: UFOs are flying saucers.

Many different kinds of UFOs have been reported. The most common UFOs are not flying saucers but simply *nocturnal lights*, that is, lights seen at night. They are often spotted in the distance, so that the observer cannot always tell whether they are attached to any object. Writer Allan Hendry studied 1,307 UFO cases reported during a one-year period in 1976–77. He found that the vast majority of the sightings were of nocturnal lights, and most could later be identified as actual objects.

Disks that resemble flying saucers are the second most common kind of UFO reported. Many of these are also seen from quite a distance and are hard to describe in any detail. The problem with the term "flying saucer" is that people automatically assume that such an object comes from outer space. Thanks to movies like *E.T.* and *Close Encounters of the Third Kind*, many people now believe that anything called a UFO or flying saucer actually has an extraterrestrial at its controls. Just because it looks like a saucer doesn't mean it is one; it could just as easily be an airplane or a weather balloon. Remember Myth #1, and you won't make that mistake.

Yah, Sure. Maybe in 150 Million years .....

Myth #3: UFOs weren't seen until 1947.

Many people think that the first UFO was seen by a man named Kenneth Arnold near Mount Rainier, Washington, in 1947. Although it's true that the term "flying saucer" was coined after Mr. Arnold's encounter and that UFOs began to be studied in a more systematic way then, sightings of UFOs have been reported throughout history — with the same outcome as the sighting in Montvale.

For example, one medieval writer, Matthew of Paris, described an event that occurred in England on July 24, 1239. He wrote that at sunset that night

> a great star like a torch appeared. It rose in the south and climbed the sky, giving out a great light. When it was high in the sky, it turned toward the north, slowly, as if intending to take up position in the sky. But when it was about the middle of the sky, in our northern hemisphere, it left behind it smoke and sparks. It was shaped like a great head, the front part was sparkling and the back part gave out smoke and flashes.

27

One of the most interesting UFO waves, or series of sightings, took place in the United States during 1896 and 1897. The UFO sighted during this period has come to be known as the "great airship," since that is how it was consistently described. It was a large cigar-shaped object with a control cabin attached to the underside. The object was seen by thousands of people across the United States between November 1896 and May 1897, and although no one knows what it was, many scientists have guessed that an engineer succeeded in constructing an airship and for some reason decided to tell no one.

Myth #4: Only crazy people see UFOs.

Nothing could be further from the truth. Studies of UFObservers have shown that they are normal, everyday people. As one UFOlogist put it, "Anyone can see a UFO — though it is likely to be a once-in-a-lifetime experience." The problem is not with the observer but with the proof. There may be a real encounter, but one person's testimony means nothing unless there are other

Hah Hah

witnesses. Even when a number of witnesses see something, attempts to verify the encounter must be made. When proof is hard to come by, some people may say that the experience never happened and that it was all in the observer's mind.

Farmers, police officers, military personnel, and teachers are said by some UFOlogists to have seen more UFOs than people in other professions have. Farmers are well represented simply because they live in isolated areas, where UFOs are more likely to appear. Police officers are also well represented, because they are often called on to investigate strange encounters. Military personnel usually spot UFOs around military bases, a known hangout for UFOs. As for teachers, perhaps they are likely to display curiosity and observe things carefully.

Myth #5: UFOs don't exist.

This is the most important myth of all. Many people refuse to believe that real UFOs exist. They think that UFOs are like Santa Claus and the tooth fairy.

Some scientists say that there are too many kinds of UFOs to be believable, that they don't fit into a neat pattern. They say that UFOs defy the laws of physics: UFOs have been reported to make sudden sharp turns while flying that are impossible in any aircraft known today. Therefore, these scientists say, UFOs cannot exist.

But UFOs do exist. Thousands of people around the world have reported seeing them. And many governments have at one time or another set up special committees to study them. From 1947 to 1969 the United States Air Force collected about 13,000 UFO reports, before deciding that UFOs did not pose a threat to national security. Notice that the air force did not say that UFOs did not exist. Even now the United States government acknowledges that UFOs may be real, for the National Aeronautics and Space Administration (NASA) has a regulation (14 CFR 1211) that allows the government to detain, examine, and decontaminate anyone who comes into contact with a UFO or its occupant. If the person does not agree to be detained, he or she can be fined up to $5,000 and sentenced to a year in jail.

Besides the United States, almost every major country has groups devoted to studying UFOs. The fact that UFOs have been seen by so many people proves that they exist; no one can deny the reality of what many people have said they've seen. This does not prove, however, that UFOs are alien spaceships.

Tell someone that you're interested in the subject of UFOs and they'll think that you believe in flying saucers. What you must point out is that you are curious about flying objects that are unidentified. These objects may or may not be related to outer space.

To help you increase your knowledge about UFOs, the next five chapters will take you through the steps for acquiring basic UFO information. You'll learn the three categories that UFOlogists use to discuss UFOs and the four kinds of close encounters a person might have. Then you'll take a closer look at real UFOs, that is, flying objects that have never been identified: their shapes, their occupants, and their missions. Once you have mastered these facts, you'll be ready to learn the mechanics of UFOlogy.

3. The ABCs of UFOs

Now that you know some of the myths about UFOs, you're ready to study the facts. In order to do this, you will need to learn the three categories used to describe UFO sightings.

First, here are five incidents. Some may have involved real UFOs, some not. As you read this chapter, you will see how UFOlogists have categorized each sighting.

1. A woman sees a glowing red ball hovering in her back yard.

2. Large circular areas are found flattened in farm fields, with no apparent explanation.

3. A flashing ball of light awakens a woman, passes through a closed window, and moves mysteriously through her house.

4. A man, his son, and their dog are on a boat when some strange aircraft pass overhead and discharge radioactive material. The debris injures the son and kills the dog.

5. A helicopter pilot in the Army Reserves is followed by a strange lighted object one night. Although the pilot tries to avoid colliding with the object by making a sharp descent, the helicopter is pulled closer to the object and the cockpit is bathed in green light.

HINT: Only one of the five encounters involves a real UFO. Keep reading for the answer.

To understand UFOs better, you will want to think of them as falling into three very different categories.

Category 1: UAP

Unidentified atmospheric phenomena (UAPs) are UFOs that are produced by natural causes. Rather than being actual objects, some UFOs are simply strange lights, called "earth lights" by UFOlogists. These UAPs include earthquake lights (lights that appear before, during, and after earthquakes) and will-o'-the-wisps (fiery lights seen in marshy areas). According to author Paul Devereux, other earth lights are still unidentified but seem to be related to bodies of water, sources of power, and openings in the earth.

One somewhat common UAP has been identified as *ball lightning*. This phenomenon occurs very rarely, but it has been reported often enough that it now has a label. It looks like a round, glowing red-orange or blue ball and usually occurs when thunderstorms are near, though this is not always the case. It may make an unusual noise and be responsible for strange electrical happenings. In fact, it seems to form near electrical wires. In the air it may move quite rapidly, but near the ground it travels more slowly. It may explode, although it usually just disappears without a sound. Whatever it does, ball lightning is dangerous.

One case reported by astronomer and UFO investigator Walter Webb occurred on July 4, 1986, in Winchester, Massachusetts. It had rained lightly throughout that day, but then the sky turned darker and looked more threatening. At 2:20 P.M., Mrs. Domenica Falcione happened to glance out her kitchen window and spot a strange, red, glowing object hovering above some evergreen trees in her back yard. She was amazed at the sight and watched as the sphere remained perfectly still for perhaps thirty seconds. To make sure that her eyes weren't playing tricks on her, she turned away for a moment. When she looked back, the red ball was still hanging in the air.

Suddenly Mrs. Falcione heard an explosion, and her house shook. The burglar alarm and the automatic lawn sprinklers began to work. She ran to the garage to check the meter box for the lawn sprinkler system; it was black and smoking, and the wall it was mounted on had been damaged.

In fact, the explosion had done a great deal of damage. A neighbor's tree had been blown apart. A foot-deep hole had been gouged below Mrs. Falcione's back fence. Her furnace and television set had burned out, and half of the fuses in the main fuse box were damaged. Altogether, Mrs. Falcione had to pay almost $2,000 to repair the damage.

An encounter with an alien UFO? Not quite. Astronomer Webb concluded that the culprit was ball lightning.

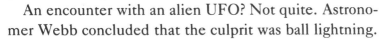

Another recurring UAP in recent years has been referred to by UFOlogists as *mystery circles*. These circles have appeared in fields, mainly since 1981, and although they have been observed in many countries, including the United States, they have been seen most often in England, usually between May and September.

The circles have been photographed for a recent book, entitled *Circular Evidence*, by UFOlogists Pat Delgado and Colin Andrews. The circles have many different formations. Most common are single circles, but sets of five are also found. None, however, are ever exactly alike. The only common denominator is that the corn or wheat crop is flattened but never damaged. Rather, the crop is swirled down to the ground.

What are these mystery circles?

Some people think that tricksters have selected isolated fields and mashed down the crop. As Delgado and Andrews have shown, however, the circles are flattened in a swirl and have different layers within the overall pattern. No footsteps are found.

A more plausible theory is that the circles are caused by a natural phenomenon known as a vortex, or whirlwind. Others believe that strong electromagnetic fields deep in the earth may account for them. Either theory would help to explain why no two circles are the same, since wind currents and electromagnetic fields vary.

Still another theory is that the circles are created by spaceships. If UFOs are responsible for them, however,

then each circle has been created by a different UFO —
quite unlikely, considering that thousands of circles have
been found. Unless there are an equal number of different UFOs, at least some circle patterns would be re-
peated.

No one has been able to prove any of these theories,
because no one has seen a mystery circle appear; they
always seem to develop overnight. To make matters
even more confusing, some strange events have been
associated with them. People have had nocturnal encounters with UFOs only to discover the next day that
a mystery circle has formed near the spot of the incident.
And in at least one case, a configuration of circles was
said to be related to a plane wreck.

On August 22, 1987, a set of four mystery circles was
found in a cornfield near Winterbourne Stoke, England.

U.F.O. VIEW of RINGS at WINTERBOURNE STOKE

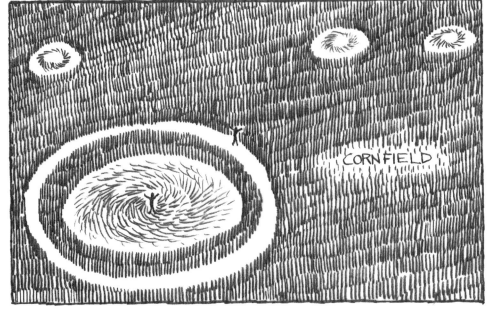

Eight weeks later, on October 22, a British fighter jet flown by Pilot Humphrey Taylor Scott left Dunsfold Airfield on a solo test flight. Six minutes after takeoff, air traffic controllers lost contact with Pilot Scott and alerted other aircraft in the vicinity. The crew of an American military transport observed the fighter a short time later. What they saw stunned them: the cockpit canopy — and the pilot — were missing! The American plane followed the jet for about four hundred miles, until it crashed into the Atlantic Ocean.

What happened to the pilot? A day later his body was found in a field not far from Winterbourne Stoke. According to UFOlogist Colin Andrews, something had happened to Scott above the field with the four mystery circles. The jet apparently changed its course by a few degrees over the circles, a fact reportedly confirmed by the British Ministry of Defence. That's when the pilot left the aircraft, but the ejection seat was not found on the ground.

Although the Royal Air Force believes that Pilot Scott was manually ejected in a freak accident, Andrews is not so certain that the force that created the mystery circles could not also have removed the canopy from the jet, causing the pilot's death. Even though the circles were made two months before the incident, Andrews believes that the coincidence of the circles and the ejection of Pilot Scott is too great to be ignored. What do you think?

A final example of a UAP comes from UFOlogist Jennie Zeidman, who reported a strange experience involving a *nightlight* that a young doctor saw in Youngstown, Ohio, in June 1979. Dr. Lynn Moorman was spending Saturday night at her parents' house. Whenever she stayed with them, she slept on the couch in the family room. The couch was set against a wall under a large picture window.

Around three o'clock that morning, Dr. Moorman opened her eyes and noticed a flashing light outside the house. She immediately thought that it was a firefly. A moment later, as the light continued to flash, she realized that it was too bright to be a firefly.

Then the light moved toward the window and — unbelievably — through the windowpane into the room. It passed in front of her, perhaps as close as three feet. The light seemed as bright as a sixty-watt bulb. Then Dr. Moorman noticed that it appeared to have two sets of wires coming from the top and bottom.

Suddenly the family dog, who had been sleeping beside the couch, woke up and noticed the flashing light. Each time the object flashed, Dr. Moorman saw it clearly; but when the light turned off, the object was no longer visible.

Dr. Moorman was quite scared by now, even though

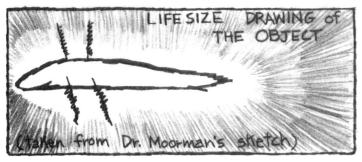

LIFE SIZE DRAWING of THE OBJECT

(taken from Dr. Moorman's sketch)

the flashing light seemed to be unaware of her and the dog. She thought about screaming, but couldn't open her mouth. When the light moved into the kitchen, she ran to her sister's bedroom. "Move over," she said. "I saw something that scared me and I'm coming into bed with you." The next morning at breakfast she told her family what had happened, but no one else had noticed anything. Her experience remains a puzzle.

Did Dr. Moorman encounter a new type of UAP? Did she imagine the object? Or did she witness a tiny UFO that had come visiting that night?

U.F.O.

Category 2: IFO

I.F.O.

Identified flying objects (IFOs) are normal objects that people mistake for something very strange. Many people have gazed at the night sky and sworn that they saw a brightly lit UFO, only to discover that it was actually the planet Venus. In one mass sighting, on New Year's Eve 1978, hundreds of people saw an object in the skies over Western Europe. Some said they saw a long tube like a railroad car; others described a glowing ball of light streaking across the sky. Many believed the object was a solid metallic shape with windows. Despite what people thought, what they actually saw was the re-entry of a booster rocket from a Russian satellite that had been launched a few days earlier. An interesting feature of this IFO sighting, according to UFOlogist Jenny Randles, was that many of the observers refused to believe the official explanation. They believed that they had seen a UFO, no matter what the facts were.

Perhaps one of the best examples of a UFO-turned-IFO occurred off Maury Island near Tacoma, Washington. On June 23, 1947, Harold Dahl, his teenage son, their dog, and another man were on a boat that Dahl used to take supplies around the Tacoma harbor. As they approached Maury Island, two aircraft flew overhead and ejected some radioactive material, which crashed onto the boat. Dahl's son was injured and the dog was killed.

From the start there was great interest in the Maury Island affair. UFOs must have been involved, it was said, because the material that crashed onto the boat was radioactive. Dahl had managed to photograph the aircraft, but the negatives were damaged by the radiation. Samples of the radioactive material were analyzed; clues started to turn up. The two aircraft were not flying saucers but government planes. In 1947, just as today, the disposal of nuclear waste was a matter of importance. Near Tacoma was a government plant that extracted plutonium from radioactive ore. The waste material was difficult to dispose of, so the Atomic Energy Commission had begun flying planes over Puget Sound and Tacoma harbor. Dahl had seen two government planes dumping atomic waste illegally. So his UFOs quickly became IFOs.

Category 3: TRUFO

Real unidentified flying objects are sometimes called TRUFOs (as in True UFOs). These cannot be explained away as atmospheric phenomena or IFOs. They are what most people think of when they hear the term "UFO": flying saucers and aliens. However, there can be other explanations for TRUFOs, as you will see.

One of the most interesting and well-studied TRUFO encounters took place over Mansfield, Ohio, in 1973. Captain Lawrence J. Coyne was the pilot of the crew of an Army Reserve helicopter that left Columbus on the evening of October 18 on a flight to the home base of Cleveland. The sky was clear but moonless that night, and visibility was approximately fifteen miles.

Near Mansfield the crew noticed a strange red light. Sergeant John Healy saw it first, to the west, but it seemed to be moving away, so he said nothing. About three minutes later, Sergeant Robert Yanacsek saw a small red light to the east, where it appeared to be moving along with the helicopter. Then the light began to move toward the copter.

Fearing that they were about to collide, Captain Coyne thrust the control stick down, and the helicopter began a quick descent. At the same time he requested information from the Mansfield control tower on jet aircraft in the vicinity. However, radio contact was lost, and the helicopter's compass began to spin out of control.

The red light continued to close in, even though the helicopter was in a rapid descent. Suddenly the light began to hover in front of and slightly above it. Coyne, Healy, and Yanacsek each later reported that he saw a cigar-shaped gray metallic object, which filled the entire front windscreen of the helicopter. This object had a red light in front and a white light at the tail. But its most interesting feature was the green beam that came from its lower portion. Without warning, the beam rose up and flooded the helicopter's cockpit with green light.

After a few seconds, the object sped away to the west. As the crew watched the white taillight recede, each man noted that the object made a sharp forty-five-degree course change, something impossible in present-day aircraft.

COURSE OF THE MANSFIELD, OHIO OBJECT

Most amazing of all, even though the helicopter had been in a steep descent, Captain Coyne noticed that it was now higher than its original altitude and still climbing. He tried to regain control of it. In a moment he felt a bump, and he began a slow descent to the cruising altitude of 2,500 feet. Coyne was convinced that something had caused the helicopter to rise quickly, even though the control stick was thrust down. That something, he was certain, was a TRUFO.

When UFOlogist Jennie Zeidman became involved in the case, she spent many hours interviewing the helicopter crew and also tried to find witnesses to the sighting on the ground. Her persistence paid off when, fifteen years later, she located a family who claimed to have personal knowledge of Captain Coyne's experience.

The Elias family lived below the general flight path to the Mansfield airport and directly beneath the route of the helicopter's flight that night. Although they did not actually see the UFO, Mrs. Jeanne Elias and her fourteen-year-old son John did hear the helicopter. The sound was so loud that Mrs. Elias, who had just gone to bed, thought the craft was going to crash and instinctively stuck her head under the pillow. Later, she laughed with embarrassment as she told Zeidman how foolishly she had reacted.

The sound wakened John, but his reaction was different. He thought, "Wow, a helicopter is hovering over the house." Then he watched as a mysterious green light illuminated his bedroom momentarily. John told Zeidman that the green light shone long enough "to make me realize that there was something above the house . . . shining a light down on the ground, or around the house, because it was coming in so heavy in my room."

Some skeptics thought that a meteor caused the helicopter's strange encounter. But as UFOlogist Zeidman concluded, the fact that the incident lasted for a long time and involved a green beam of light proved that a meteor was not its cause.

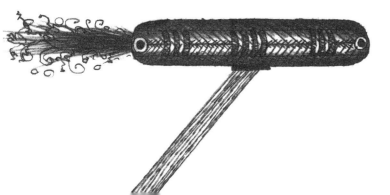

4. Four Kinds of Close Encounters

The next step in learning about UFOs is to be able to identify the kinds of close encounters a person might have with a TRUFO. A close encounter (CE) is a fairly rare occurrence, since most sightings take place at a great distance. However, CEs have happened often enough to be categorized. UFOlogist J. Allen Hynek described three kinds of CE in his 1972 book, *The UFO Experience*; around 1980, a fourth kind, one that is more frightening, has been added by other UFOlogists. If you happen to see a TRUFO, you'll want to be able to identify the kind of encounter you've had.

Close Encounter of the First Kind: Close Sighting

A Close Encounter of the First Kind, or CE-1, is the most common type of UFO experience. A CE-1 is any

close-range sighting that occurs without tangible evidence: no trace of the craft is left, no creatures are seen. Without proof, the experience is impossible to study. Yet a CE-1 is hardly boring.

One CE-1 occurred on Interstate 70 near Indianapolis on March 29, 1978. Three trucks were traveling together on the highway; the truckers were talking to one another on their CB radios. Suddenly the trucks were covered with a bright blue light, as if a giant spotlight from the sky were shining on them.

The drivers couldn't see beyond the hoods of their trucks, and everything was silent. The CBs stopped working, and the engines of the three trucks began to run roughly. This lasted for perhaps five seconds. Then the blue light blinked off and things returned to normal: road noises, CBs, and engines. The drivers were stunned, but one man announced on his CB, "Hey, UFO, if you have your ears on, I want to go with you."

As if someone were listening, the blue light covered the trucks again, this time for fifteen seconds. The three engines ran into trouble again, and the trucks lurched and slowed to 10 mph. When the light stopped the second time, it did not return.

48

Other people witnessed this strange incident. A woman who was across the highway told the truckers on her CB that "it looked like a big bright blue lampshade over the three trucks."

Close Encounter of the Second Kind: Physical Evidence

A CE-2 is commonly called a "physical trace" encounter, since the UFO leaves behind some kind of evidence that it landed. This kind of encounter has the potential to prove that UFOs exist. In actual practice, though, most CE-2s have provided little substantial evidence.

Two types of CE-2 exist. In a Type 1 episode, the person does not actually see the UFO, only the results of its landing. In a Type 2 episode, the person sees not only the results but the UFO itself — at close range, so there can be no doubt that the witness is observing a TRUFO.

One of the most studied Type 2 physical-trace encounters took place in Delphos, Kansas, on the evening of November 21, 1971, and was researched by UFOlogist Ted Phillips, among others. A sixteen-year-old boy named Ron Johnson was working on his parents' farm. About seven o'clock, he was in the sheep pen with his dog. Without warning, he heard a rumbling sound ("like an old washing machine," he told investigators later) and saw a brightly lit mushroom-shaped object about seventy-five feet away. It was hovering a few feet from the ground, glowing with a steady mass of lights, not individual lights. Ron and his dog remained silent, though the sheep began to bellow. The bright lights hurt Ron's eyes.

The base of the UFO lit up with even brighter lights, and the craft moved at a forty-five-degree angle over the hog shed. Ron was blinded by the intense light and heard the UFO zoom away like a jet plane. Moments later, when he was able to see again, he saw the UFO in the southern sky. He ran to the house and told his parents what he had witnessed. With them, he returned to the yard, and they watched the UFO light grow smaller in the sky.

Then Ron showed them where the UFO had hovered. Even in the darkness of the November night, they could see a luminous gray-white ring. Some nearby trees also seemed to glow. The Johnsons touched the soil ring: it was cool and slick. But Mrs. Johnson said that her fingers

50

became numb, and when she wiped her fingers against her pants, her leg also became numb. Both Mr. and Mrs. Johnson experienced prolonged numbness over the next few weeks, while Ron developed headaches and some eye trouble. He also began to have nightmares.

Investigator Phillips checked for other possible witnesses and found none. He also made sure that samples of the glowing soil ring were sent to different laboratories for analysis. Unfortunately, the findings at some laboratories contradicted the findings at others, and the results must be called inconclusive.

Close Encounter of the Third Kind: UFO Occupants

A Close Encounter of the Third Kind (CE-3) occurs when a person makes contact with a UFO and its occupants. A CE-3 that received almost no publicity in the United States took place in Rendlesham Forest, England, in late December 1980. Because the case is far from solved, it is still very controversial, so this version of the events may not be the final word.

Rendlesham Forest is located near two Royal Air Force bases that are leased to the United States. Because of the sensitive nature of operations at the two airbases, great care is taken to secure the area surrounding them.

On December 27, 1980, a group of air force security officers saw what they thought was a small aircraft heading for the forest. This was so close to the base that it had to be investigated, and two security officers walked into the woods.

There, in a clearing, they came upon a kind of green fog. It rose from the ground to a height of about three feet and seemed circular. Through it they could see the ground and some cows on the other side. As one of the security officers said later, "It was like nothing I'd ever seen before."

The two officers tried to find the aircraft that seemed to have fallen, crashed, or landed in the woods, but found nothing except the fog. Suddenly a red ball of light sailed over the trees toward the clearing and stopped above the fog. Then the red ball burst into a spray like a large chrysanthemum firework. When the lights dissolved, the green fog had disappeared and a large wedge-shaped UFO standing on three legs was in the clearing.

The men watched the object for a while and even tried to approach it. Each time they did, the UFO rose about six feet and moved away. One of the men saw what he thought were aliens. "There was definitely something inside it," he said later. "I don't know what. But the shapes did not look human. Maybe they were like robots."

Time and time again the two men attempted to touch

the craft. Each time the UFO retracted its legs and flew
a short distance away. It made no noise and maneuvered
easily through the trees.

Eventually the security officers were joined by other
air force personnel, perhaps thirty in all. The men
formed a ring around the UFO, with fifteen-foot spaces
between them. But the object took off without warning.
The cows and some forest animals went into a frenzy,
rushing away from the site. An hour later the UFO was
spotted near the rear gate to the airbase. Then it disappeared.

The air force investigated afterward and discovered triangular indentations at the site as well as high radiation levels in the indentations.

But the story does not end there. Supposedly, three nights later the UFO returned. This encounter is described in much less detail than the first, and some say that it never occurred at all. If it did, this is what some sources report:

The UFO, damaged in some way, returned. More airmen went to the woods, and this time they saw three UFOccupants. The creatures were small humanoids, identical to each other, dressed in silver suits. A beam of light that fell from under the craft allowed the three creatures to float in the air. Wing Commander Williams ordered everyone to stand back as he approached the aliens. Apparently he was able to communicate with them without using any speech. Soon the craft was repaired. It took off slowly, then quickly sailed toward the North Sea.

The CE-3 at Rendlesham Forest raises many questions and answers none. Perhaps the most important question is, did it happen at all? Because all of the witnesses were military personnel, most did not want to speak publicly. Those who did risked exposing themselves to ridicule. Could the whole account have been made up by a few bored airmen? Could it have involved a secret military aircraft? Or did the encounter with UFOccupants really happen? Eventually, with additional study, we may learn the truth about the Rendlesham Forest CE-3.

Close Encounter of the Fourth Kind: Kidnapped!

The newest close encounter is one that involves the kidnapping of a human by a UFO. While the idea may surprise and trouble you, this is the most common type of close encounter reported in recent times. Many UFOlogists, even those who would like to prove that TRUFOs come from outer space, view CE-4 reports with a great deal of disbelief, since it is impossible to prove that these experiences ever really happened. To them, it seems more likely that the person had a dream and thought it was real.

Most CE-4 cases have many things in common. They all seem to begin with a sense of "missing time." The person who is kidnapped is aware of seeing or doing something; then, in the blink of an eye, he finds himself in another location or position and realizes that a certain amount of time (ten minutes? two hours?) is unaccounted for. Later the person may have nightmares, and his behavior or personality may change.

One of the most thoroughly researched CE-4 cases occurred at a summer camp near Burlington, Vermont. According to astronomer Walter N. Webb, Michael Paine and Janet Ashford were working at a summer camp named Buff Ledge, which is now closed and abandoned. Most of the campers and staff were away on August 7, 1968, and Michael and Janet were looking forward to spending the day relaxing. Just after sunset, when they were sitting on a dock that jutted into Lake Champlain, they noticed a brilliant light, which arced toward them. As it did, they could see that it was not a star but a cigar-shaped object. It stopped, and three small white lights emerged from one end of the cigar. The large UFO departed and the three satellite ships put on a dazzling aerial display. Janet and Michael watched in awe.

Two of the satellites zoomed away, but the third flew quickly toward the dock, stopped about sixty feet away, and hovered fifteen feet above the water. This satellite ship, as big as a house, was disc-shaped and had a transparent dome. According to Michael, two beings were visible through the dome. One of them seemed to talk to Michael, while the other was in control of Janet.

"You will not be harmed," Michael was told. "We have come from a distant planet. We have made earlier visits to Earth and returned after the first nuclear explosions." The small UFO moved to within twenty feet of the dock. Michael jumped up to try and touch it. As he leaped into the air, a white beam of light covered both him and Janet. Michael said later that he was "filled with light," and he and Janet floated up to the UFO.

57

In the UFO, Michael watched as the creatures carried out an examination of Janet: a small piece of skin and a blood sample were taken. Then he was led to a table next to Janet's. As he lay on the table, he could look up and see the stars and the moon through the dome of the satellite UFO.

Michael has no memory of what occurred next, but when he awoke, he found himself back on the dock with Janet. The small UFO hovered above them.

A voice in Michael's head said, "Don't worry about this experience: nothing bad happened. We are friends. We care about you. You will not understand much of this experience. Janet won't remember anything."

Another voice said, "Janet is all right. Goodbye, Michael."

Suddenly Michael heard car doors slamming as the campers returned for the evening. The UFO turned off its lights and sailed out of sight. Janet seemed dazed and incoherent, and Michael helped her to her cabin before heading for his.

Once in their cabins, both Janet and Michael fell asleep immediately. When Michael awoke about an hour later, he wanted to talk to Janet, but her cabin was off-limits to boys. Since they worked in separate areas of the camp, they did not meet the next day. Instead, Michael tried to tell some of his friends about the incident. When they wouldn't believe him, he decided against talking to Janet about the experience. She didn't seem to remember anything about it, for she did not mention the encounter when he finally saw her a few days later. After a few more weeks the camp closed for the season. Janet and Michael never met again.

Not until ten years later, when Michael felt that he had to report the incident, did anyone know about the encounter. Interviewed separately in different cities, and hypnotized, he and Janet confirmed to Walter Webb the story of their abduction by the small domed satellite of the cigar-shaped UFO.

What really happened to Michael and Janet? Did they share a dream? If you think so, when was the last time you shared exactly the same dream with someone? If you think Michael and Janet were lying, why would Michael wait ten years to talk about the UFO? And why would Janet agree with him? This is another case you will probably be hearing more about.

5. Flying Cigars and Other TRUFOs

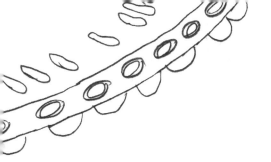

The FIVE MAIN TRUFO SHAPES

1	2	3	4	5
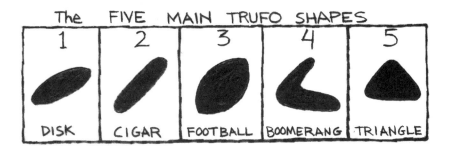				
DISK	CIGAR	FOOTBALL	BOOMERANG	TRIANGLE

You may think of flying saucers when you think of UFOs, but there are many different sizes and shapes of TRUFOs, including some described as "flying flower-pots." However, only a few have been seen in any great numbers. Descriptions of the five main TRUFO shapes follow.

TRUFO Type 1: Flying Saucers or Disks

The most common type of TRUFO reported is the flying saucer or disk. A flying saucer may look like a doughnut with a dark center, two saucers facing each other, or a saucer bottom with a domed top. It can be small or large, with a variety of lights. According to UFOlogist Mark Rodeghier, who has studied TRUFOs that have followed or otherwise interfered with automobiles, a disk-shaped TRUFO is usually described as a metallic object that produces sound and gives off a white beam of light.

Danish UFOlogist Kim Hansen has researched many TRUFO sightings. Perhaps one of the most interesting involved a disk-shaped UFO in Imjärvi, Finland, on January 7, 1970. Two men, Aarno Heinonen and Esko Viljo, were skiing in a rural area of southern Finland. Around 4:45 P.M. they stopped at the bottom of a small hill to catch their breath. The sun was setting, and a few stars had become visible. Suddenly a strange buzzing sound began, and the two men noticed a reddish gray cloud streaking across the sky. As the cloud came closer, the sound intensified.

When the cloud was about fifty feet from the ground, Aarno and Esko could discern something inside it: a round, flat-bottomed metallic object. As it approached the ground, both men saw a dome on its top. Then they noticed a tube that extended slightly from the center of the bottom. Without warning, a beam of bright light from the tube illuminated the ground.

The men stood motionless. It was at this point that they saw the creature.

"I think I took a step backward," Aarno reported, "and in the same second I caught sight of the creature. It was standing in the middle of the light beam with a black box in its hands. Out of a round opening in the box there came a yellow light, pulsating."

What exactly did the creature look like?

Almost three feet tall, it wore light green overalls and dark green boots. Its face looked pale and waxen. It was quite thin and seemed to have claws rather than fingers. It wore a cone-shaped metallic helmet.

The creature aimed the opening of the black box toward Aarno, and the reddish gray cloud spread over the men. Red, green, and purple sparks began to fly from the center of the beam of light. Esko said that many of the sparks hit him, but he felt no pain. The cloud became so thick that the men could not see the creature or each other, even though they were just a few feet apart. All of a sudden, the light beam flew up from the ground like a flickering candle flame, and the UFO and the mysterious cloud disappeared. Both men estimated that they had seen the creature for no more than twenty seconds. For perhaps three minutes more they stood there mesmerized.

Aarno gradually became aware that his right side, which had been closest to the light, was numb. In fact, as he tried to take a step, his right foot felt as if it had been shot full of Novocain. He toppled over, unable to keep his balance.

Eventually Esko was able to drag his friend home. A doctor was called when Aarno complained of aches and pains throughout his body, including severe headaches. Surprisingly, the doctor could not find anything wrong with him, even though he developed some very strange symptoms that lasted more than six months. He had difficulty with his memory and sometimes forgot how to get home after he went out. The doctor admitted that Aarno's symptoms could have been caused by exposure to radioactivity, but he did not have the proper instruments to test this theory. A professor of physics at Helsinki University, Dr. Matti Tuuri, suggested that Aarno's symptoms were similar to those caused by an overdose of x-rays.

Was the story true?

The men could offer no proof of their encounter. Scientists who studied the site of the incident discovered nothing, not even signs of excessive radiation. Still, two other, unrelated people had reported a UFO the night of Aarno and Esko's encounter. And when the two men visited the site six months later, along with three journalists, the journalists' hands inexplicably turned red. As Matti Haapaniemi, a local farmer, said, "Many people in their neighborhood have laughed at this story. But I don't think it's anything to joke about. I've known Aarno and Esko since they were little boys. Both are quiet, rational fellows, and moreover they are abstainers [from alcohol]. I'm sure their story is true."

However, Aarno has reported seeing twenty-three other UFOs since 1972 as well as speaking to at least two UFOccupants. Presents given to him by these space creatures mysteriously vanished when he was asked to produce the evidence. When he tried to photograph a female UFOccupant, Aarno reported, she disappeared along with his camera.

UFOlogist Hansen rightly doubts Aarno's later encounters. But could the first encounter with a UFO have caused Aarno to imagine other such meetings? Or did Aarno and Esko simply make up the first encounter, and their illnesses as well? If so, what did they hope to gain? These contradictions demonstrate why the study of UFOs can sometimes be exasperating.

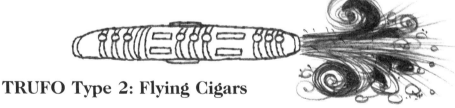

TRUFO Type 2: Flying Cigars

The second most common type of TRUFO is the flying cigar. It is long and narrow, much like the body of a jet plane; sometimes people say that one end emits smoke.

Flying cigars have been reported in many colors. Some UFOlogists believe that they are really metallic and that their color is only a reflection of the sky or the sun.

One of the most recent major sightings of a TRUFO involved a flying cigar. This series of encounters, reported by UFOlogist Don Schmitt, occurred in Belleville, Wisconsin, beginning in January 1987. According to Schmitt, the first few people to sight the object saw a triangle of lights. Officer Glen Kazmar of the Belleville Police first saw them around 8:00 P.M. on January 15, while on patrol. At first he didn't think much about them, since he knew that planes from the Milwaukee airport frequently flew over the area. Around 3:00 A.M., though, he and his partner saw many more lights. They had driven up the highest hill in the county where they witnessed a "close-knit cluster of red, blue, and white lights." The two men reported the unusual sight, but the Milwaukee airport could confirm only that it was tracking a slow-moving object that was not in voice contact.

That might have been the end of the encounter if other witnesses had not observed the mysterious lights. In fact, at least three independent reports were phoned in to local police departments. All of them described a cigar-shaped object flying over and in front of drivers in their cars.

Schmitt heard of the various reports and set out to investigate. First he eliminated the possibility that the

UFO was either a UAP or an IFO. No planes were reported in the vicinity, and no unusual atmospheric conditions were present.

As he tried to find an explanation, other sightings occurred. Perhaps the strangest was reported by Harvey Funseth and Fred Gochenaur, who were driving north of Belleville on Friday, March 6, when they spotted four strange objects in the sky to the west. What they saw startled them so much that they stopped their car to get a better look.

One of the objects was quite large and resembled the mysterious flying cigar. While it was in the air, its position was straight up. Positioned directly beneath it were three other, much smaller objects. Funseth and Gochenaur thought that these objects were sections of the larger cigar.

Suddenly the cigar-shaped object changed position and began to fly horizontally. It did not look like any plane the men had ever seen: there were no wings or tail — just a fuselage. Its only other noticeable characteristic was a red glow from the rear, like a rocket without flames. It streaked out of sight toward the northeast.

What can be made of this series of sightings? As Schmitt concluded, "We could not certify that spaceships were visiting the area, but we were certain that UFOs — whatever they are — were."

TRUFO Type 3: Flying Footballs

Another frequently seen TRUFO is shaped something like a football, or perhaps the Goodyear blimp. Many witnesses report seeing flying footballs with domes or portholes; some see both. Sometimes the objects are covered in metal, sometimes in a quilted clothlike material.

A well-documented case of a flying football TRUFO, which was reported by writer Margaret Sachs, occurred in Red Bluff, California, on August 13, 1960. What is particularly interesting about this sighting is that at least fourteen police officers observed the UFO at one point or another.

The episode began near midnight, as Tehama County Highway Patrolmen Charles Carson and Stanley Scott searched for a speeding motorcyclist. As they raced down Hoag Road, a large object appeared in the sky in front of them. Believing that it was an airplane about to crash, they quickly stopped the patrol car and jumped out. Instead the officers saw a football-shaped craft that they later estimated to be about 150 feet long and 40 feet high. It gave off a white glow and had small red lights at each end.

As Carson and Scott watched, the UFO flew slowly about 200 feet from the gound, then reversed direction and accelerated. It varied its speed, hovered, climbed

68

higher, and flew low — as if it were performing aerial stunts in a strange kind of circus!

Each time the UFO seemed to stop near the patrolmen, they tried to approach it. As soon as they stepped toward it, however, the UFO moved away, as if it knew the men were attempting to contact it. Twice, though, it flew toward their patrol car, illuminating the area with a beam of red light. Both times the radio in the car did not work when the patrolmen tried to radio for help. Finally the UFO began to move slowly toward the east, but only after Officer Scott turned on the patrol car's red light.

Carson and Scott followed the UFO in their car at a safe distance. They were surprised to see another UFO, similar to the first, approaching from the south. It joined the first; then both of them stopped, hovering in the sky. Eventually, they flew off together and disappeared in the east.

By the time this encounter was over, it had lasted more than two hours and had been tracked on radar by a local airbase. Besides the two patrolmen, witnesses included the night jailer at the Tehama County jail and even several prisoners who were allowed onto the roof of the jail to watch this strange occurrence.

Although the air force suggested that Carson and Scott had observed Mars and two bright stars, UFOlogist Sachs concluded that these could not have accounted for the sighting, since all three were below the horizon at midnight. Concerned about the air force's conclusion, Officer Carson, who had served in the air force, said: "Both of us were aware of the tricks light can play on the eyes during darkness. . . . We find it difficult to believe what we were watching, but no one will ever convince us that we were witnessing a refraction of light."

TRUFO Types 4 and 5: Boomerangs and Triangles

Two other kinds of UFOs have been reported in substantial numbers. UFOlogists are not certain whether these TRUFOs are the same object seen from different angles.

A series of encounters with a boomerang-shaped UFO occurred in the Hudson Valley, north of New York City, from 1982 to 1984. The object became known as the Westchester Boomerang, since so many sightings took place over Westchester County.

One of the earliest encounters occurred on February 26, 1983, and involved Monique O'Driscoll and her seventeen-year-old daughter, Maureen. According to UFOlogists J. Allen Hynek and Phillip J. Imbrogno, the two women were driving on an isolated country road around eight o'clock that night when Maureen saw some lights on a hill. Both women knew that there was no house on that hill. Then the lights started to move along the treetops.

"I was entranced," Monique told investigators later. "What really caught my eye was the brightness of the lights, and the way the object was moving so slowly. There must have been fifty lights."

Monique and Maureen began to follow the UFO. Suddenly it passed directly over the car. Monique stopped, and she and her daughter watched as the UFO hovered over a nearby lake. Monique wanted to get a better look and left the car.

The UFO's lights, all flashing wildly, reflected off the ice on the lake. The object itself was large, perhaps 200 feet across, and its surface reminded Monique of a bridge with crisscrossed beams of metal. Despite its size and apparent weight, the UFO made no noise whatsoever. Monique stood at the edge of the lake and watched for a few minutes, then the UFO began to move away.

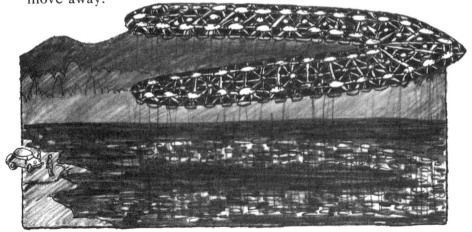

"Oh, please don't go," Monique said to herself. "I want to look at you some more." Just then the UFO stopped, changed direction, and began to move slowly toward her.

"It's gonna take us!" Maureen yelled.

Monique reported that she had mixed emotions about the UFO at that moment. She wanted it to come closer, but she was also afraid that it would harm her. As she began creeping back toward her car, the UFO took off in the opposite direction.

Other people reported seeing the Westchester Boomerang that night, and during the next two years many had sightings similar to the O'Driscolls'. Some also reported that they felt the enormous UFO was watching them and knew what they were thinking.

On March 31, 1983, in Sandy Hook, Connecticut, near the New York border, Cindy Tillson was watching television with her great Dane, Thunder. It was about 8:30, and Cindy hadn't bothered to turn on any lights yet. Suddenly Thunder started to bark wildly. Though she tried to calm him down, he wouldn't stop. Finally Cindy got up and walked into the kitchen, where the dog pawed the sliding glass doors.

Cindy immediately saw what was disturbing him: a brightly lit, brown, boomerang-shaped object. She watched it for a while, trying to decide what she was seeing. A fire? It was bright enough. A truck? It appeared to have headlights, but they were enormous. And it was

in the air. Nothing made sense.

Then Cindy turned on the outside floodlights. The UFO moved to the left. She flicked off the lights and the UFO moved back to its original position. She turned the lights on again, and the UFO moved to the right. Confused and now scared, Cindy turned the lights off for good; she felt that the UFO was watching her.

"I made sure everything in the house was off because I wanted to stay hidden," she told investigators. Then she watched as a wide beam of light projected from the bottom of the object. As Cindy said, "It looked like it was trying to see something below." Finally she telephoned a relative, but the UFO had disappeared by the time she hung up. All the while, Thunder had barked at the object. The next day he would not go outside.

Although hundreds or perhaps thousands of people reportedly saw the Westchester Boomerang and various photographs of the object were taken, no one knows for

73

sure what it was. Some thought a formation of light air-craft was responsible for creating a UFO hoax, but it is doubtful that airplanes could have continued to fool people night after night. While the object might have been a long-lasting UAP, still unknown to scientists, it is just as likely that it was a TRUFO.

UFOlogist John Timmerman has described a woman's encounter with a large triangular UFO near Lima, Ohio, on February 12, 1986. Mrs. Larson was awakened after midnight by an indescribable sound. Her first thought was to check her daughter's room to make sure that she was all right, but her daughter was sound asleep. Then Mrs. Larson glanced out the window in her front door. She saw strange lights above a neighbor's house. More curious than frightened, she opened the door for a better look. She quickly discerned a triangular object hovering in the sky. It had a red light on top and a white light on the bottom corners. Unlike many UFO cases, the lights were steady, not blinking.

Mrs. Larson witnessed the giant triangle for two minutes. Although she had been awakened by a sound, she was not aware of any sound coming from the UFO now. By the time she roused her husband, the object was gone.

An astute observer, Mrs. Larson told Timmerman later that the UFO appeared "to be a very large object with a very dark central exterior and a slightly lighter perimeter. I could see the shape and body of the object against the slight glow in the lighter background sky. 'Big,' 'massive,' and 'heavy' describe what I saw."

Timmerman attempted to verify the sighting. In order to turn Mrs. Larson's UFO into an IFO, he contacted the Allen County sheriff's office, the Ohio State Highway Patrol, and the local airport for any possible explanations, all without success. He even placed a newspaper ad searching for witnesses. But no one else had seen the strange object that night.

As is the case with many UFObservers, Mrs. Larson was not interested in UFOs and had never read any books about them. She had a master's degree in counseling and worked in a local nursing home. Was she dreaming, or did she see a TRUFO? What do you think?

Remember, these are the most common types of TRUFOs reported. That doesn't means that a UFO you see won't look very different from these. You just might be the first person to spot something completely new.

6. Who's Who Inside TRUFOs

If you ask people what UFOccupants look like, some will invariably answer, "Little green men." A look at UFO reports, though, shows that many different kinds of UFOccupants have been sighted over the years.

Although most reports don't describe little green men, such creatures have been observed. UFOlogist Jenny Randles, in her book *The Pennine UFO Mystery*, relates the story of two strange green beings that were reportedly seen in 1912 by two children on the Isle of Muck in the Scottish Hebrides.

The children were accosted on the beach by two small "people" dressed in green. These creatures spoke both English and Gaelic, and according to the children cast a spell on them. They asked the children many questions about their life and their family and then pointed to a small, strange-looking craft floating offshore, which held another small being and a dog. The two green creatures asked the children to board the boat, but before they could do so, their sister arrived and saw them staring out to sea. The sister did not see the boat or the beings. As she approached, the two youngsters seemed to wake up from a dreamlike state. Only then did they display any fear about what had happened to them and realize the mystery surrounding their encounter.

So little green men have been reported occasionally. Other creatures, though, are much more common. These are the next step in learning about UFOs. There are at least four usual kinds of UFOccupants, and there are many differences within a given type. Do these reports mean that UFOccupants actually exist? Did people imagine them? Or have we been visited by creatures from other planets? You'll have to decide for yourself.

UFOccupant Type 1: The Small Humanoid

Many people have seen UFOccupants that they describe as dwarflike or small. These small humanoids are reportedly three or four feet tall and have round heads (which might be helmets) and long arms that reach to or below the knees. They are usually seen wearing metallic space suits or coveralls. People who have met them say that they appear to be scientists, here to study mankind. They are not known for their friendliness.

78

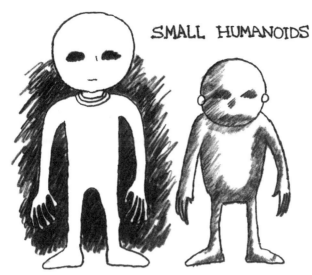

SMALL HUMANOIDS

UFOlogist Richard Hall interviewed a doctor who claimed to have examined the corpses of dwarflike UFOccupants who crashed on Earth. Doctor X stated that the cadavers he examined had openings rather than ears, lacked any teeth, had no internal organs and no blood (only a colorless liquid), and were covered with tan or gray skin.

One incident involving small humanoids took place in Newark Valley, New York, on April 24, 1964. At ten o'clock that morning, farmer Gary Wilcox was working in a field near his house. The field was on a hill, and at the top, half-hidden behind some trees, was an old refrigerator. Gary saw something shining as he looked toward the ridge of the hill. He assumed that it was the refrigerator reflecting the sun — until he realized that the shining object was closer to him than the refrigerator. Curious, he drove his tractor up the hill, all the while watching the shining light.

As he approached it, he saw that the object was bigger than a car and somewhat oval. At first he thought it might be part of an airplane, but an inspection revealed that it wasn't. It had no seams or rivets and was made from a strange material that seemed to be a combination of metal and canvas.

Two men, wearing seamless white overalls and having no facial features, emerged from under the egg-shaped object. Each held a square tray filled with alfalfa, roots, soil, and leaves. Gary was certain that someone was playing a practical joke on him, but he soon changed his mind.

"Don't be alarmed," one of the men said. "We have spoken to people before."

What Gary noticed immediately was that the voice seemed to come from *around* the man rather than from *within* him.

"We are from what you know as the planet Mars," the man continued. Then he told Gary that they came to Earth every two years.

"People should not be sent into space," the man warned. He said that two astronauts, John Glenn and Virgil Grissom, and two Russian cosmonauts would die within a year, because they had traveled in space.

"Do not mention our visit," the other man said. With that, they returned to their ship.

Gary heard the craft make a noise like a car engine idling. As the noise diminished, the ship took off silently to the north.

Most people might not have reacted so calmly, but Gary merely drove home, called his mother, and told her about the encounter. Then he milked the cows and finished his chores. By the end of the next week, word had spread, and a police investigation was carried out on May 1, 1964. Gary was even tested by a psychiatrist to determine whether he had been suffering from any hallucinations that day. The doctor concluded that Gary was a truthful person.

Perhaps most surprising was the creature's prophecy. Although it was not fulfilled precisely, Virgil Grissom, along with two other astronauts, died in a fire on an Apollo rocket on January 27, 1967. What's more, on April 23, 1967, a Russian cosmonaut was killed when his re-entry parachutes failed to open. Was the prophecy related to these two events? No one can ever know for sure.

Another case took place on the morning of January 4, 1979, in Rowley Regis, England. According to UFOlogist Jenny Randles, Jean Hingley had just said goodbye to her husband when she noticed a bright light in her garden. Then she heard a strange sound: *Zee, zee, zee.*

As she looked up, she saw three strange beings fly into her living room. They fit the description of the dwarf humanoid exactly: three and a half feet tall, with white, waxen faces, thin mouths, and no eyebrows.

Suddenly Jean found herself floating toward them. "I had my hand on the door," she said later, "but my feet didn't touch the floor." She floated into the living room,

where the creatures were inspecting the Christmas tree.

You will not be harmed, she was told. The creatures didn't use any words, but seemed to communicate with her telepathically.

"Where are you from?" she asked.

We come from the sky, she was told. *We come down here to talk to people, but they don't seem to be interested.*

For some reason, Jean thought she would show them how to light a cigarette. As she struck a match, the creatures fled to the garden, where their oval UFO was sitting. They floated into the craft, and it departed.

Afterward Jean noticed that the electric clock had stopped and that all of her cassette tapes had become magnetized. She felt sick and complained of sore eyes for a week. No one else reported seeing the UFO or the creatures, but a team of local police did discover an indentation where an oval craft might have landed in her garden. The indentation was perfectly preserved in a covering of light snow, and photographs of the landing site were taken by a local UFO group. This was the only proof Jean had that her UFO experience was real.

UFOccupant Type 2: Humanlike Beings

Other people have seen more normal-sized UFOccupants, often reported to be six feet tall or more. These beings have been described as coming in colors ranging from white to brown; on rare occasions green skin has been reported, though this may be due to a green uniform that gave a green cast to the creature's skin. The beings' eyes have been described as dark, large, and deep-set, although others have said the eyes were pink or blue and catlike. Many have pale blond hair and are called beautiful in a strange way. These beings are friendly, and people who have an encounter with them usually feel quite positive about it.

One such encounter took place near Frodsham, England, on January 27, 1978, about 5:45 P.M. The day was cold and the sky had grown dark. Four teenage boys decided to do some illegal hunting of pheasant on private property.

They were near the River Weaver, in an area known as the Devil's Garden. As they waited in the undergrowth to snare a pheasant, they saw something following the surface of the river, approaching and then passing them. It was ball-shaped, silvery, and about twenty feet above the water, and it made a slight humming sound.

Because of recent reports of a Russian satellite that had crashed in Canada, the boys' first thought was that they were seeing some kind of satellite. Whatever it was, they knew they were observing something quite strange.

The silver sphere had a flashing light on each side, near the top. What appeared to be a row of windows circled it near the middle, emitting a purplish light that was hard to look at.

When the object landed in some nearby bushes, the four hunters became frightened — not so much by the object as by the possibility of being contaminated by radioactivity from a satellite. Then they saw a figure, which looked human and was wearing a silver jumpsuit and helmet. Attached to the top of the helmet was a blinding purple light similar to a miner's lantern.

The young men watched as this creature surveyed the

84

scene and gazed at some cows in an adjacent field. The cows seemed to be entranced by the silvery ball. The figure stepped behind the ball, out of sight of the four boys, and returned seconds later with a companion, similarly dressed. The two figures carried a large cage made of light metal. They walked toward one of the cows and, using the cagelike contraption, appeared to measure it.

By now the hunters were terrified. They feared they might be next on the list if the beings caught sight of them. They turned and ran, not looking back until they were a mile or so downriver. You won't be surprised to learn that they could not see anything more of the mysterious silver sphere or its occupants.

Why should we believe this strange close encounter? First, the young men were engaged in an illegal activity. It's unlikely that they would volunteer information that put them in danger of arrest unless they truly believed that they had seen something quite remarkable. Second, they sought no publicity for themselves. They would not allow investigators to report their names and did not seek any monetary gain from their adventure. Third, all four testified to the story. Finally, at least three other sightings or encounters with a similar craft were reported in that same area during January 1978.

Another encounter with humanlike aliens, described by UFOlogist Willy Smith, occurred in Isla de Lobos, Uruguay, on October 28, 1972. Isla de Lobos is a small island, important only for its lighthouse, which is operated by the Uruguayan navy. Five men are stationed on the island to attend to the electric generators. On that night, they had finished dinner and played a few games of cards when Corporal Fuentes noticed that it was time to inspect the generators. It was just after ten o'clock and completely dark. As Fuentes approached the lighthouse, he noticed an object with bright lights on the terrace beside it. His first thought was that he was seeing an automobile, but that was impossible; the only people on the island were the five naval officers. He was so concerned that he returned to the officers' building for a pistol.

As Corporal Fuentes headed toward the lighthouse again, he observed the lights carefully. They were yellow, white, and violet, and they lit up the area so well that he could see a figure standing next to the object.

Then two more figures descended from the UFO. Fuentes judged them to be five to six feet tall. He could not make out what they were wearing, but he noticed that they seemed to walk in slow motion.

Fuentes was perhaps one hundred feet away when the three beings noticed him. They stood on the terrace, six feet above him, and stared. Frightened, Fuentes attempted to shoot, but he could not raise his arm. He could only watch as the beings entered their vehicle, which lifted straight up, humming slightly. Then it tipped a little and a fireball burst from under it. The craft shot off silently to the southeast.

None of the other men on the island believed Fuentes's story. However, he was sent to see a higher-ranking officer, who listened to his story and brought two American Embassy personnel to interview him. Why people from the American Embassy would want to interview the corporal is puzzling, especially since the American government has gone to great lengths to discount the possibility of UFOs. He was also interviewed by a UFO organization, which concluded that he was telling the truth.

UFOccupant Type 3: Robots or Machines

Although sightings involving mechanical creatures are less common than other kinds, they are the most unusual encounters recorded. Almost no two accounts of robots and machines are similar. Each case appears unique and special.

One example occurred in Livingston, Scotland, on November 9, 1979. Bob Taylor was patrolling a forest area near the main highway between Glasgow and Edinburgh. His job that evening was to look for stray animals. Bob parked his van and got out to check the area on foot. Accompanying him on his rounds was his dog, Katie, a red setter.

Everything seemed normal until Bob walked into a small clearing and saw a dome-shaped object. It was twenty feet wide, metallic, and had a row of antennas ringing its circular base. Suddenly portions of the object began to fade away, becoming transparent. Bob could actually see through them to the forest background. Then the encounter turned ominous.

Two gray balls emerged from the object. About as large as basketballs, these spheres had sharp spikes, perhaps six inches long. The two balls resembled landmines or giant maces, and they behaved like robots.

88

The balls rolled toward Bob, and before he could even think about moving, they were beside him. He felt a tug on his legs. At the same time he became aware of a terrible, gaseous odor. Then he passed out.

After what he took to be a few minutes, he regained consciousness. He was lying in mud with Katie by his side, but the object and the gray spheres were gone. Bob tried to stand, but his legs wobbled. At that point he began to realize that he had been hurt in some way. He was very thirsty and had a severe headache. His van had a two-way radio, but he was unable to call for help. He also found it difficult to drive; eventually he left his van in a ditch and walked a mile and a half home.

There, as he removed his muddy clothes, he noticed that his pants, which were made of the heavy cloth commonly used in police uniforms, had been torn on both hips. The tears seemed to suggest that the spheres had used their spikes to tug him toward the domed object. If this was true, the spheres had been quite gentle, since there was only a small scratch mark on his skin.

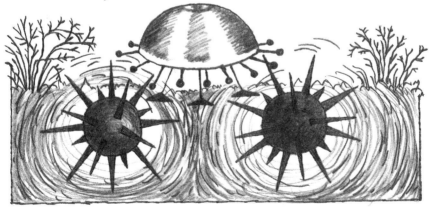

Many questions about his encounter remain. Were the gray spheres responsible for Bob's injuries? Had they dragged him to the domed object? Was the object a UFO? Did the site produce any evidence that a UFO had existed?

Seven police officers examined the forest clearing. Between the time that Bob reported the encounter and the time of the investigation, though, there had been a heavy snow, so the investigators slowly removed the snow.

What did they find? First, a set of triangular indentations that looked as if they had been made by the legs of some machine. This might be where the domed object rested on its landing gear. They also discovered two small tracks of gouged earth where Bob had been pulled headfirst toward the object. Perhaps something had interrupted the attempt, because it seemed that he had been pulled only partway. Finally, they found perhaps twenty or thirty holes, which matched Bob's description of the spheres' spikes.

UFOlogists can only assume that Bob stumbled across a UFO. His description of the site corresponded to the evidence that the investigators found. But beyond that, nothing proved his encounter except his insistence that what had happened had been real.

Were the gray balls really robots? Why were they interested in Bob Taylor? If they were responsible for dragging him, why did they stop? And who, or what, was inside the domed object? Bob's boss, Malcolm Drummond, who inspected the alleged landing site, commented: "Bob is not a man to make something up. If he said he was attacked by some creatures, then there must have been something there."

An even more frightening encounter occurred on January 27, 1977, near Prospect, Kentucky. A nineteen-year-old boy named Lee Parrish had been visiting his girlfriend that night. When he left her house about 1:00 A.M., he knew he had a seven-minute ride home in his Jeep. As he drove west on Highway 239, he saw an object hovering above the tree line, perhaps a few hundred feet from the road and one hundred feet in the air. The object was rectangular and its blazing red color was hard to look at. Still, no matter how he tried, Lee couldn't stop staring.

Within fifteen seconds, the Jeep's radio stopped working. By then the Jeep was directly underneath the object. Lee said later that he wasn't even driving his Jeep, that it managed to stay on the road without his control. Suddenly the UFO sped away to the northwest like a jet without sound.

When Lee arrived home, his mother was still up.

"What's wrong with your eyes?" she asked.

Lee glanced in a mirror and saw that his eyes were badly bloodshot. He was also aware for the first time that they stung. Then he noticed that it was 1:45 A.M. His seven-minute trip home had taken forty-five minutes.

He told his mother about his encounter. She in turn called a local UFO group. She could tell that something very real had happened to her son, but neither she nor Lee had any idea exactly how terrifying an experience Lee had really had with the fire-colored UFO.

The next day Don Elkins and Carla Rueckert interviewed Lee about his experience and arranged for him to be hypnotized to determine what had happened during the forty-five-minute ride home. Where had all the time gone? Had he passed out? Or had something else happened?

Here is what Lee told them under hypnosis:

When the UFO hovered above Lee's Jeep, he became quite frightened. In his trance, he kept repeating, "It's not moving, it's not moving." The UFO had caught the Jeep and pulled it into the air, using a powerful force field. Then Lee felt something in his eyes. When his eyesight cleared, he was no longer in his Jeep but in a round, immaculately white room. He had no idea how he had arrived there, but he knew he had not left the Jeep by way of the door.

In the room were three objects. To his left was a large black slab that had a small rounded area on top, so that it looked like a three-dimensional silhouette of a man. This black object had a mechanical arm. To his right was a red object the color and shape of an old-fashioned Coca-Cola vending machine. It too had an armlike extension. Directly in front of him was a large white rectan-

92

gular object, perhaps six feet high, with a square wedge positioned like a head. Although none of the three objects resembled a robot, let alone a life form, Lee was certain that they were living. He was also certain that the white robot was the leader.

The black robot's arm moved toward Lee and touched his back. The red robot's arm touched him on his right shoulder and above his right ear. The touch of both robots hurt. Then the three robots disappeared, leaving Lee alone in the white luminous room. Suddenly he found himself back in his Jeep, driving home. Within five seconds of the UFO's disappearance, the Jeep radio began to work again.

Elkins and Rueckert drew no conclusions about this episode; they merely let Lee tell his story. What adds credibility to his account is the fact that the electrical system on the Jeep malfunctioned the day after his encounter with the UFO and required extensive work.

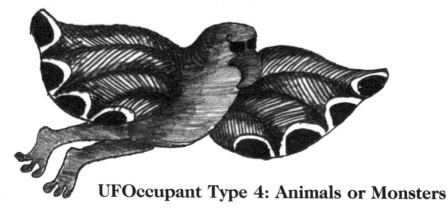

UFOccupant Type 4: Animals or Monsters

This is perhaps the strangest category of UFOccupants and, fortunately, the least likely to be seen. One animal/ monster, reported frequently in one Ohio Valley area in 1966 and 1967, was Mothman. Like a combination of Superman and a hawk, this creature was featherless but winged and reportedly could fly as fast as a speeding car without flapping its wings.

Other UFO monsters have been reported as well. One appeared in Flatwoods, West Virginia, on September 12, 1952. A group of children were playing outside at sunset when they saw what they thought was a meteor landing on a hill nearby. The children decided to investigate the strange light. They saw a large ball, which one boy described as "as big as a house." One of the children heard a throbbing sound, while another heard hissing. Another boy in the group saw a pair of eyes gleaming in the shadows. He shined his flashlight toward the eyes to scare the animal away. Just as he did, all the children saw a giant creature, over ten feet tall, with a blood-red face and glowing orange-green eyes. They watched in silence as the creature began to float slowly toward them.

94

Before it reached them, they ran back down the hill, screaming for help.

The next day the editor of the local paper scouted the hill for signs of a UFO landing. He found a number of marks on the ground and a large round area of flattened grass. He also noted a strong, pungent smell. As with so many purported UFO landings, nothing else was turned up.

Finally, strange beings are sometimes observed *after* a person has witnessed a UFO encounter. Because these beings are usually dressed in black, they are called the Men in Black, or MIBs. They have been seen most often in the United States. Supposedly, they travel in groups of three in large black automobiles. They say that they are FBI or CIA agents, military personnel, or telephone workers. Whoever or whatever they are, their aim has been to silence anyone who reports UFO encounters, mostly by intimidating the person. Since there have been relatively few encounters with MIBs, many UFOlogists now believe that such reports were either hoaxes or the illusions of people who became frightened after seeing a UFO.

7. TRUFOccupations

THE COW JUMPS OVER THE MOON.

The final step in learning about UFOs is knowing what TRUFOs do. In a typical encounter involving UFOccupants, a person sees a TRUFO as it lands. Then one or more UFOccupants come out, perform some activity, and reboard the TRUFO. Finally, it takes off. But what exactly do UFOccupants reportedly do when they emerge from their crafts?

UFOccupation #1: Collecting Samples

When you go on a vacation, you often bring home souvenirs. That seems to be the case for UFOccupants, too. Of course, you might be likely to buy a T-shirt, whereas UFOccupants are interested in other kinds of mementos. For example, cattle and other livestock seem to be

97

at the top of UFOccupants' souvenir lists; many reports of UFOs stealing cattle have been logged.

One such report was made by Alexander Hamilton of Yates Center, Kansas, who claimed that on April 23, 1897, he saw a huge airship land near his farm. His sighting occurred during the "great airship" wave. According to Hamilton, he and two other men raced to the airship and found "six of the strangest beings I ever saw. They were jabbering together, but we could not understand a word they said." Then the airship lifted off, taking with it one of Hamilton's cows. The next day a local farmer found the remains of the stolen animal.

Hamilton wrote: "After identifying the hide by my brand, I went home. But every time I would drop to sleep I would see the cursed thing, with its big lights and hideous people. I don't know whether they are devils or angels or what; but we all saw them, and my whole family saw the ship, and I don't want any more to do with them."

You should know that Hamilton was a former Kansas senator, and that his story was attested to by twelve prominent men from Yates Center. For years many UFOlogists pointed to Hamilton's story as one that proved the existence of UFOs. But what no one knew, until UFOlogist Jerome Clark did some research recently, was that Hamilton and the twelve men were members of the local liars club! They had managed to perpetrate a hoax that lasted over eighty years.

Many less suspicious reports of UFOs stealing cattle and other items have been made. One of these came from Rosedale, Australia, according to UFOlogists Bill Chalker and Keith Basterfield. About 1:00 A.M. on September 30, 1980, a farmer was awakened by a strange whistling noise. His livestock were obviously troubled; there was great turmoil in the horse barns and cattle pens.

The farmer hurried outside and saw a large flying disk moving across his farmland close to the ground. He watched as the disk hovered over a ten-thousand-gallon water tank, then landed just beyond it. He was worried about his animals, and about the strange craft now resting on his property. He quickly got dressed, jumped on his motorcycle, and headed toward the UFO.

As he rode, he could still hear the shrill whistle, and when he was within fifty feet or so of the UFO, the sound became so high-pitched he had to cover his ears. Then he was knocked down by a rush of hot air. The object had risen and flown away. In moments the livestock calmed down. In the moonlight the farmer could see the ring where the disk had rested. The next morning he could easily see a brown circle twenty-eight feet across, with six spokes inside it. What's more, the entire water tank was now empty. The UFO had drained the tank, according to the farmer.

Did the UFO take the water as a souvenir? Or was it conducting a large-scale scientific experiment?

UFOccupation #2: Making a Rest Stop

Have you even taken a long drive across the country? You can't go too far before you need to stop for gas or a bathroom or sometimes a repair. Think of UFOs the same way. If they do come from galaxies millions of light-years away, they may need to make a rest stop.

One famous encounter occurred in Eagle River, Wisconsin, on April 18, 1961. Farmer Joe Simonton walked outside his farmhouse at 11:00 A.M. and saw a metallic-looking flying saucer hovering close to the ground. Joe later described it as being twelve feet high and thirty feet around.

As Joe watched, the UFO landed and a door opened. Joe saw three olive-skinned men with black hair sitting inside. They were about five feet tall and were dressed in black turtlenecks and knit helmets.

What did these three UFOccupants want? One man held up a jug, which appeared to be made from the same material as the UFO. The men indicated that they wanted Joe to fill it with water.

100

When Joe returned to the UFO, he handed the jug to the first man and gestured that they could now drink. At the same time he noticed that another man was cooking some food on a grill. The men must have misunderstood Joe's gesture, for they gave him three of the items they were cooking. What was this strange, otherworldly food? Pancakes.

In a few minutes the UFO departed, and Joe called the local authorities. No proof of the encounter was found, but Joe stuck by his story. He also had two of the pancakes; he had eaten one, though it tasted like cardboard. Another was sent to a laboratory for testing. Was it made out of strange chemicals and compounds? Unfortunately, its ingredient list read like the one on a package of pancake mix.

As a result, some UFOlogists have concluded that Joe had a dream that morning and was unable to tell the difference between his dream and reality. Others are not so sure, including the local sheriff, who had known Joe for fourteen years and who believed what Joe was telling him.

Why would a man lie about seeing a UFO and UFOccupants who were handing out pancakes? It would be safer to keep such a story private. Some UFOlogists believe that this helps prove the experience was real.

Joe Simonton's farm may have been one of the first reported rest stops for intergalactic visitors, but it hasn't been the last. A very different kind of rest stop was made by a UFO in New Berlin, New York, on November 25, 1964. In an account reported by Ted Bloecher, Mary Masson described her experience that night.

Mary's husband had gone deer hunting, and when she couldn't sleep, she put on a coat and stepped outside. "I was looking at the stars and trying to figure out where the constellations were, and I noticed a falling star," she told Bloecher. "Then I saw another one."

Within a few minutes a brightly lit UFO landed on a hill near Mary's house. Although she couldn't see the top of the vehicle, the bottom appeared disk-shaped and sat on legs. Then she noticed a team of five UFOccupants carrying boxes or chests. They appeared to be wearing something like dark skin-diving suits. They were muscular and quite tall, and she assumed that they were men.

"The were working on this vehicle like I've seen my father work on farm machinery," Mary told UFOlogist Bloecher. "They seemed to have wrenches and screwdrivers, and tools . . . a man would use to work on a piece of machinery."

Joined by her mother-in-law, Mary watched for a while. Then the UFO was joined by another. About five UFOccupants from the second craft joined the first team. Together the two groups of men removed what appeared to be a motor from the underside of the first UFO. With a great deal of difficulty, they worked on the object for the next three hours. Throughout the

102

time, Mary was convinced that she was being watched by the UFOccupants. Even her mother-in-law said later, "I can't explain it, but . . . I am sure they realized that we did not call the authorities, that we weren't going to."

By five in the morning, the men had replaced the motor and quickly re-entered the UFOs. Both shot off, "almost like an instantaneous disappearance," according to Mary. The next day she searched the landing spot. She found two separate sets of three indentations where the UFOs' legs had rested. She also found a piece of material the men had used in their repairs. It looked and felt like aluminum, but Mary was sure that it wasn't. For six years or so after the sighting, Mary and her mother-in-law kept quiet about their encounter. By the time they were interviewed, the strange piece of "aluminum" had disappeared. But Mary would never forget her encounter with a broken-down UFO.

UFOccupation #3: Inspecting

UFOs and their occupants have shown an interest in many different kinds of manmade objects. They seem

103

to want to know how things work. At the most basic level, UFOs have a fascination with automobiles. Perhaps the most likely encounter a person can have takes place while riding in a motor vehicle. This can be quite frightening, especially if the witness believes that the UFO is following the vehicle.

For example, truck driver Harry Joe Turner was driving a truckload of ketchup through Virginia on August 28, 1979. According to Turner, the engine, the headlights, and all of the electrical components of his rig conked out at about 11:15 P.M. He saw bright lights shining in his rearview mirror, and a dark object passed overhead.

As his truck coasted along without power, traveling nearly seventy miles an hour, the door to the cab opened and someone grabbed him by the shoulder. Turner had a revolver with him. He shot at the intruder but did not harm him. Then he passed out at the wheel.

When he came to, he was certain he was going to crash. Then he realized where he was: parked at his destination in Fredericksburg, Virginia, seventeen miles from where the intruder had appeared. Even more puzzling was the fact that all of his gasoline had been used up. The two radio antennas on the cab of his truck were burned, and one had been cut off.

Laboratory analysis revealed nothing special, but Turner remains convinced that his experience really happened. He was later able to remember what occurred after he passed out in his truck. His truck was lifted into a large UFO, where he was greeted by human-sized creatures in white clothes and caps. Most surprisingly, he claims that he was taken on a tour of the universe.

After his experience, he became a very religious man.

UFOccupation #4: Watching People

UFOccupants have also shown an interest in people. One of the more frightening cases of this sort happened on September 4, 1964. Three men who were hunting for deer with bows and arrows near Cisco Grove, California, separated in the woods. One of the men, Donald S., who has never allowed his last name to be published, became lost and lit three campfires to signal his friends.

Donald saw a light and assumed it was his friends searching for him, but he grew frightened when he realized that the light was flying toward him. He climbed a large tree and watched the light as it flew around the tree. There was a flash, and a domed object dropped to the ground, hidden by some manzanita brush.

Donald couldn't believe what he was seeing, especially when two creatures approached the tree. Because the moon was out, Donald could see that they were wearing silver uniforms with helmets. They looked directly at him with enormous black eyes. Donald sat still and watched as a robot joined the creatures. This robot had large glowing orange eyes, and white smoke or vapor came from the rectangular hole that must have been its mouth. Suddenly Donald couldn't breathe, and he passed out.

A short time later he awoke, still in the tree but nauseous. The two helmeted creatures were trying to climb the tree. Not knowing what else to do, Donald took his bow and shot three arrows at the robot. Why not at the two other creatures? Perhaps he wasn't thinking clearly. Each time the arrows knocked the robot backward and created a bright flash on impact.

Then Donald began throwing things at the creatures. Since he was out of arrows, he threw his bow at them, then his canteen and some coins. When he had nothing left, he took off some of his clothing, ripped it into pieces, and set them afire before dropping them on

the creatures. First his cap, then his outer camouflage
jacket, and finally his inner heavy jacket went down in
flames. After each fiery piece of clothing fell, the creatures would back away and then approach again. At the
same time the robot kept blowing the white smoke at
Donald as if to gas him.

All night Donald managed to thwart them. At dawn,
however, a second robot joined the siege. The two robots moved to the foot of the tree. Sparks suddenly
bounced between their midsections. They sent a large
cloud of smoke into the tree, which caused Donald to

pass out once more. This time when he awoke he was alone, his clothing in shreds and burned. He felt exhausted and sick. As he later discovered, he had survived a 38-degree night without heavy clothing. Eventually Donald found his friends. One of them had also seen a large, glowing light that night.

Because this is one of the few examples of aggressive UFOccupants, some UFOlogists want to believe that Donald was the victim of a cruel trick. It seems unlikely, however, that anyone could have played such a joke in a remote area. How did his companions conjure up a UFO and two robots? No matter how difficult it is to believe, it's more likely that a real UFO was there. The fact that Donald suffered suggests that he didn't manufacture the encounter himself. He also avoided all publicity afterward, unlike many people who have tricked authorities about possible UFOs.

Fortunately, this type of episode has been extremely rare.

UFOccupation #5: Observing the Military

UFOs have shown an interest in modern warfare and its technology. This has led some UFOlogists to conclude that they may be secret spy planes from other countries. Others believe that UFOccupants from other worlds are concerned about the damage nuclear war on Earth might do to the universe.

Many sightings have taken place in and around U.S. Air Force bases, including Loring AFB in Maine and Wurtsmith AFB in Michigan. A typical sighting occurred on November 7, 1975, at Malmstrom AFB in Montana. Malmstrom happens to be a launch site for Minuteman missiles, and on that day the alarm sounded at one missile silo. A sabotage team quickly went to the site and saw a large orange disk hovering over the area. Two jet fighters stationed at Great Falls, Montana, were sent after it, but the disk disappeared from radar before they could intercept it.

Could the disk have been a figment of the men's imaginations? According to UFOlogists Lawrence Fawcett and Barry Greenwood, all members of the sabotage team were sent to the base hospital for psychological testing. Hospital personnel determined that the team members had experienced a traumatic event.

The missile itself was inspected from top to bottom by other specialists that day. They found one puzzling piece of information. The target for each missile, indicated by a number, is recorded on a computer tape. Surprisingly, the target number for the missile inspected by the UFO had somehow been changed. Was the UFO responsible? Although no one can say with certainty that it was, the missile was replaced.

The next day there were more sightings, but each time the jets flew toward the missile site, the UFO disappeared. During the next eight months, 130 UFO reports were recorded in the area of Malmstrom AFB.

What did the air force have to say about this breach of security? Helicopters were responsible, the press was told. But how could helicopters outmaneuver jet fighters? And how could a helicopter be mistaken for a large glowing disk? One pilot said, "The weather was so bad when the report came in that it would have been impossible to fly a helicopter."

UFOs have also appeared with regularity during wartime. If you have read much about UFOs, you will know the story of the foo-fighters in World War II. Foo-fighters were strange yellow-orange lights that appeared to fly alongside bombers; they were seen in both Europe and Asia during the war. In fact, as UFOlogist Richard Hall points out, every major war since World War II has included UFO sightings.

For example, in June 1966 at Nha Trang, a coastal base in South Vietnam, a burst of bright light at 9:45 P.M. was followed by the appearance of a UFO. The UFO lowered itself to within a few feet of the ground, in plain view of many soldiers. At the same time the electrical generators failed and the base lost all of its power and lights. Airplane, bulldozer, and even diesel truck engines all stopped working for about four minutes — until the UFO shot straight up into the air and disappeared.

UFOccupation #6: Continuing the Mystery

Whatever UFOs and their occupants do or don't do, one thing can be said with certainty: UFOs never do anything that would help to solve the mystery of what UFOs are and where they come from. So perhaps their primary occupation is not to collect samples or conduct inspections but to puzzle the citizens of Earth.

Only dedicated investigators can try to solve the UFO mystery. The second part of this book will show you how.

TEENAGE JOY RIDERS

PART II
Becoming a UFOlogist

8. How to Catch a Flying Saucer

Now you know what many people have reported about UFOs. Before you start looking skyward, though, you will want to do some further reading and research. Then you'll be ready to hunt UFOs.

1. Increase your knowledge by reading.

You can do this in a number of ways. First, read all the UFO books in your school library and your local library. This will give you more information, usually about the most popular UFO cases.

Second, you can probably find information about nearby UFO sightings at your local library. Ask the librarian if there is a special file on UFOs. Some libraries have a file room or cabinet for newspaper clippings on subjects of local interest. If yours does, you're in luck. You might also ask if your local newspaper, which will be stored in the library, has an index. If it does, you can search for any UFO stories that have been published.

Depending on where you live and what kinds of UFO activity have taken place there, you may find a rather large amount of material in your library. Read what you find and ask yourself the following questions:

Have sightings taken place locally?
When did the sightings take place?
At what time of day did the sightings occur?
Have any sightings been reported in the same area?
What kinds of UFOs were sighted?
What kinds of UFOccupants have been reported?

Finally, you may want to subscribe to a UFO magazine, which will keep you posted on the most recent sightings. One is the *International UFO Reporter*, which is published every other month by the Center for UFO Studies (CUFOS). You can check on the cost of a subscription by writing to CUFOS at 2457 W. Peterson Avenue, Chicago, Illinois 60659. Another magazine is *UFO*, 1800 S. Robertson Blvd., Box 355, Los Angeles, California 90035.

2. Practice your powers of observation by improving your ability to describe.

"It was big and gray with four things on the bottom, and it had two white curly tubes that stuck out of the front and it was standing still." This description, supposedly

of a UFO, would not help any UFOlogist. Why? Because it's not specific enough. Reread it and think of a large animal. That's right, this might as well be an elephant as a UFO.

In a slightly better description, two eleven-year-old girls described the UFO they saw like this: "The object was white when we first sighted it, then as it moved towards the moon it changed color. As it reappeared, another similar object also appeared. They crossed paths, then moved across the sky in opposite directions until they disappeared."

What's wrong with this description? First, the girls never said what the object looked like. Second, they never said what color it changed to. Third, they said it reappeared, but never mentioned how or when it disappeared. They might also have described how long they observed the objects, how fast they were traveling, and how large they were.

To be a first-rate UFO witness, you must describe what you've seen with precision. Some practice might help. Here are some exercises. While you can practice by yourself, it will probably be more fun with a group of friends or even with your class at school.

Practice 1: UFO Saucepan. Have everyone in your group bring a saucepan and a ruler. Each person should write an exact description of his or her own saucepan. If your reaction is "I can't describe a saucepan," ask yourself how you'll ever hope to describe a flying saucer if you can't manage a saucepan.

Write down everything that will help identify your saucepan. Use your ruler and measure it, then include the measurements in your description. Look for any special markings (scorch marks, scratches) and their position on your pan. Include this information as well. Then place all the saucepans together and exchange papers. If you've done a good job of description, another person should be able to find your saucepan.

Practice 2: UFO Dimensions. Look out a window at a distant large object. For example, from your kitchen window you might be able to see a garage. Or from your classroom window you might see some playground equipment. Sketch the object and indicate in the margins how tall, wide, and deep you think it is.

Next, go outside with a tape measure and measure the object you observed. Were you close to the actual measurements? Did you guess that it was thirty feet long when it was only ten? Try to develop a good sense of size, since you will want to give an accurate estimate of any UFO you see.

Practice 3: UFO Picture. Watch the last five minutes of *E.T.*, then write a complete description of the spaceship that comes to collect E.T. If you have difficulty, remember that you may see a TRUFO for only a minute or so. You must be able to describe what you've seen, no matter how short the time you observed it.

Practice 4: UFO Directions. As a UFO investigator, you might have to draw an object that a witness describes to you. To practice this ability, have someone look at the following three pictures:

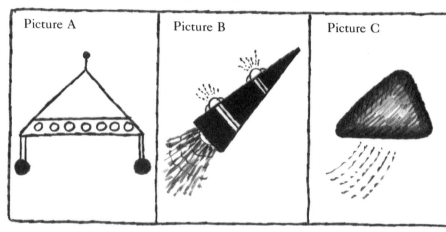

Picture A   Picture B   Picture C

This person should attempt to describe one picture in such a way that listeners can draw the object. The describer should not face the audience, because she might be tempted to use gestures. Only the describer may speak; no one in the audience can ask questions.

For example, the describer of Picture A might begin by saying: "Draw a two-inch line in the middle of your paper, going from left to right. This line is the bottom of the UFO. At each end of the line is a landing foot which goes straight down for a half inch and has a little circle at the end."

Do you understand how specific you must be in order to describe what a UFO looks like? Do you also see how well you must picture what a witness tells you? If the observer simply says, "It's a triangle," think of how many possible triangle shapes there are.

3. Refine your knowledge of UFOs by classifying UFO reports.

If you or someone you know has a close encounter, can you say with certainty what kind it was? Was it a CE-1 or a CE-3? Was it a CE-2 Type 1 or 2? For practice, reread Chapters 5 through 7 and categorize each story according to what kind of encounter it was. You may decide to create some new categories.

After working on these skills, you should be ready to see a UFO. Although there are no magic ways of making sure that you see one, there are things you can do to improve your chances. Here are seven tips for finding one.

Tip 1: Stay up late.

This may not be an idea that your parents will like, but it's a good way to have a UFO experience. According to UFOlogist Jacques Vallee, almost all UFO landings take place after 6:00 P.M. Sightings rise in number until about 10:30 P.M. and then begin to decline. Very few sightings of TRUFOs take place between 6:00 A.M. and 6:00 P.M. The number of sightings decreases after 10:30 because most people go to bed around that time. The more people there are in bed, the fewer there are to spot a UFO. Of course, some people see strange lights outside their bedroom windows, so being in bed doesn't rule out the possibility of seeing a UFO.

122

Tip 2: Be in the right place.

Most UFOs are observed by witnesses who are outside at the time. But it's not just a matter of being outdoors. Where you are may make a difference. Here's a list of the top thirteen states for UFO sightings, based on recent studies:

California

Ohio

Pennsylvania

New York

Missouri

Illinois

Indiana

Iowa

Texas

New Mexico

Kansas

Florida

Minnesota

This doesn't mean that you won't see a UFO if you live somewhere else. Your chances may be a little better in these states, that's all. What's more, a rural area in any state is better for UFO spotting than a heavily populated area. However, while it's true that you'll be less likely to see a UFO in New York City or Los Angeles or Denver or Chicago, it's also true that UFOs have been sighted just a few miles from almost every large urban area in the country.

123

Tip 3: Be young.

Many UFOlogists distrust stories told by children, but collectively, more children see UFOs than any age group of adults. Do children see more UFOs, or are they more likely to report what they see? In general, children have fewer preconceptions about things and report just what they've seen — no matter how odd it is.

Being young, however, is not the only factor in UFObserving. Other studies have suggested that people with red or blond hair are more likely to see a UFO and that left-handed individuals may also have more close encounters. But seeing a UFO is probably a matter of luck for many people.

Tip 4: Take an automobile ride.

No one knows how often UFOs have been spotted by people in cars, but many people have this experience while driving or riding. Mark Rodeghier of the Center for UFO Studies in Chicago reviewed reports of vehicles

124

that encountered UFOs and uncovered a number of facts: First, most vehicular encounters occurred on rural roads in clear weather. Second, most lasted for less than ten minutes. Third, most did not involve any UFOccupants. Finally, most of the UFObservers had trouble with their vehicle's engine, headlights, and/or electrical equipment before and during the encounter.

One example occurred in Marshall County, Minnesota, on August 27, 1979. On this clear night, Deputy Val Johnson was patrolling County Road 5 in his Ford LTD when he noticed a white light above the tree line perhaps two miles to the south. The light seemed too bright to belong to another car or a truck, so he decided to investigate. He wondered if it might belong to a light aircraft involved in a drug-smuggling operation across the Canadian border.

He turned onto Highway 220 and accelerated to 65 mph, keeping his eyes on the light. Suddenly it swept toward his windshield, blinding him. At that moment he passed out.

When he came to, he realized that his car had skidded across the highway into the oncoming lane. Fortunately, no other cars were traveling that night or he surely would have been involved in an accident. Still, Johnson was not in good shape. His head had hit the steering wheel, and his eyes felt raw and sore. He radioed for assistance.

"Something hit my car," he reported. "I don't know how to explain it. Something attacked my car. I heard glass breaking, and my brakes locked up, and I don't know what the hell happened.''

Officer Greg Winskowski arrived quickly, along with an ambulance, and Johnson was taken to a nearby hospital. He was treated for eye irritation, which the doctor said was similar to what might happen to a welder who wasn't wearing a mask, and released a few hours later.

That wasn't the end of the case, though. Sheriff Dennis Brekke inspected the site of the accident carefully. He discovered that the damage done to the patrol car (a smashed headlight, a cracked windshield, an almost broken radio antenna) could not have been caused by anything then at the scene.

What Sheriff Brekke found most interesting, though, was that the clock in the patrol car and Johnson's own wristwatch were both exactly fourteen minutes slow. By looking at the deputy's earlier radio messages that night, Brekke was able to confirm that Johnson's watch had been correct prior to the accident. What could have caused both timepieces to lose fourteen minutes?

Brekke called a nearby UFO center, but an extensive investigation proved nothing conclusive. However, some people believe that Johnson did encounter a TRUFO and somehow collided with it or with the electrical field that surrounded it. As to where those fourteen minutes went, no one knows.

While Deputy Johnson's experience is thought-provoking, it is even more amazing to compare it with an encounter that Russ Johnson (no relation to Val Johnson) had two days later, at almost exactly the same time — only four hundred miles away in Vermillion, South Dakota.

Russ Johnson saw a light ahead of him on the highway. It rushed toward him and covered his car with bright light. Blinded, he slammed on the brakes and skidded sideways to a stop. He opened his eyes and watched an object zoom into the sky behind his car.

No newspaper had yet carried word of Val Johnson's encounter, so if Russ Johnson was making up a story, he did so without reading anything about Val Johnson's experience. He did not claim to be injured and his watch did not stop.

A strange similarity? Two encounters with the same TRUFO? This is the kind of case you may be asked to handle as a UFOlogist.

Tip 5: Fly in an airplane.

Pilots and passengers in airplanes have also reported a substantial number of UFO sightings. In fact, one of the best recent encounters happened to the pilot of a Japan

127

Air Lines flight from Paris to Tokyo. This was a freight flight; JAL Flight 1628 was filled with French wine bound for Tokyo. After a stop in Iceland, the plane continued over Greenland, Canada, and finally Alaska, where it was scheduled to stop at Anchorage. However, as it entered Alaskan airspace late in the afternoon of November 17, 1986, Captain Kenju Terauchi realized that the lights he was observing to the bottom left of his windscreen were unusual.

What was strange about them? First, they appeared to be lights from two fighter planes. Second, they appeared to be following the JAL flight. Third, they were about 2,000 feet below JAL 1628, which ruled out the possibility that they were stars that Terauchi had misidentified.

After seven minutes or so of watching the lights, Terauchi reported, "Two spaceships stopped in front of our face, shooting off lights. The inside cockpit shined brightly, and I felt warm in the face."

These UFOs were aligned vertically and appeared as rows of lights in a rectangular pattern. They stayed clearly visible in front of the plane. The entire flight crew watched as the UFOs began to put on a light show with what appeared to be exhaust jets. The display was so colorful that Takanori Tamefuji, the copilot, compared it to Christmas lights.

The crew decided to contact Anchorage to report what was happening. Although air traffic controllers in Anchorage did not initially pick up any strange objects on

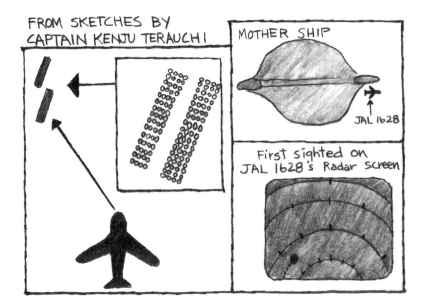

FROM SKETCHES BY
CAPTAIN KENJU TERAUCHI

MOTHER SHIP

JAL 1628

First sighted on
JAL 1628's Radar screen

their radar, the plane's radar indicated that a large object was following five miles behind. Later, however, Anchorage confirmed the appearance of an unknown aircraft in JAL 1628's vicinity.

When Terauchi was interviewed, he drew for investigators his own interpretation of what had happened: a large mother ship of the two smaller spaceships had taken JAL 1628 under its wing. After about fifteen minutes, the two UFOs had moved away from the cockpit, and Terauchi had seen the dimly lit, enormous silhouette of the mother ship. Another aircraft in the vicinity, United Airlines Flight 69, closed in on JAL 1628 to observe the mystery object. But by that time the mother ship had disappeared.

This case was studied fairly thoroughly, though the Federal Aviation Administration decided not to comment on the nature of the sighting. Some skeptics wrote that Terauchi had mistaken Mars or Jupiter for his UFO. Of course, this explanation makes no sense, considering the geometric nature of the lights that Terauchi observed. Others said that the signal received by the JAL flight's radar was merely an echo of the plane's own image. UFOlogists easily ruled out stars, planets, cities, and other known aircraft as responsible for the lights. Some, however, are unconvinced that Terauchi saw a mother ship; they are more willing to believe that he saw two UFOs. Whatever happened, it is clear that JAL 1628 had a remarkable flight.

It's THEM with the breadcrumbs, AGAIN.

Tip 6: Be near a power source or reservoir.

For reasons that no one yet understands, many UFOs are reported near power lines and reservoirs.

According to UFOlogist Raymond Fowler, one power

130

plant that has been the site of a number of UFO encounters since 1952 is the New England Power Station at Salem, Massachusetts. On July 16, 1952, Shell Alpert, a member of the coast guard, photographed four oval objects hovering near this station. The commander of the local coast guard station released the photographs, much to the displeasure of coast guard officials. Although many explanations were offered by the government, none convinced Fowler.

On October 2, 1965, another sighting took place. The witness, sixteen-year-old James Centorino, was the son of a meteorology professor at Salem State Teachers College. James told Fowler that he was on his bicycle at about 8:20 P.M. when he saw two white lights shining brightly over the smokestacks. "Each stack has two red lights," James explained, "but I couldn't figure out what the white lights were. There seemed to be a dark shape between them, so I cycled down to the plant and up to the fence around it for a closer look."

From his vantage point, James could see a twenty-foot-long cigar-shaped object with a slight hump near the back. Each end had a white light, and the object hovered at a 45-degree angle above the smokestacks. As James moved closer, it made a sound "like air being let out of a balloon." Then it rose further, turned off its lights, and disappeared in the darkness. Fowler discovered that an anonymous woman also reported the UFO to police that night, and the coast guard station

131

received numerous calls. The station commander, however, would not release the names of any callers.

Other sightings have taken place at the New England Power Plant as well. Fowler believes that as a conduit of energy, it may attract UFOs. Some scientists also suspect that UAPs may form in electromagnetic fields like those found around power plants and high-voltage power lines.

Tip 7: Be patient.

Patience is a necessity for anyone interested in seeing a UFO. If you aren't expecting to see one, you might have a better chance of a close encounter. In fact, many people who have seen UFOs report that they felt compelled to look at the sky or out a window for no real reason. "I knew I had to look," a typical witness might later report.

One witness woke up at 4:30 in the morning and felt an urge to look out the window. He saw three large orange balls hovering over the lake that his property bordered. In a moment the three spheres zoomed up, and he seemed to wake up from a trance. As he turned to go back to bed, he realized that his parents were standing behind him. They had woken at the same time and felt the same urge to look out the window. Had the UFOs been communicating with them? Had the air around the lake suddenly changed? Many other people have reported similar encounters.

If you do see a UFO, the next chapter explains the complicated matter of what to do while you're watching it.

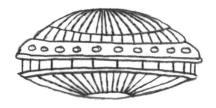

9. Observing a UFO

U.F.O. WITNESS'
BASIC
TOOLS

U.F.O.
NOTES

To be prepared for an encounter with a UFO, you will need three things: a *notebook*, a *pen* or *pencil*, and a *camera*. A spiral notebook is probably best; you can keep your pencil tucked in the spiral. As simple as these objects may be, they are the basic tools a UFO witness needs.

Let's say that you are riding your bicycle at sunset. As you are pedaling down a deserted road near an open field, you see a bright light approaching. At first you think it's an airplane or a helicopter. But as it gets closer, it looks like no flying object you've ever seen. Besides, it doesn't seem to be making any noise.

You may feel frightened, but you're also just plain curious. You quickly ride to a nearby tree for cover. You want to see everything, and you want other people to believe that what is happening is real.

The UFO hovers over the field.
What should you do?

1. Don't stop watching.

No matter what, keep your eye on the UFO. If you don't, you may regret your mistake, the way William Pokorny and his daughter Siena did. They saw a brilliant light in the sky on May 31, 1968, in Bryant, Iowa. Four months after the sighting, Siena and her father wrote to the National Investigations Committee on Aerial Phenomena about the experience they couldn't forget. Siena wrote:

> Dad first saw it by himself . . . and when it began to glow and become very bright, he called me. When first looking at it, I saw the most brightest form beyond any comparison ever seen in my life.
>
> [After] watching it for maybe two minutes, Dad said, "Quick go get the binoculars in the house." [I] was unable to find the field glasses and ran back to him.
>
> So he said he would try and find them himself and he hurried back to the house. The object was still very bright.
>
> Then . . . the baby ducks I had been taking care of began peeping so I attended to them. This is my biggest mistake. I should have kept my eyes on that thing, I realize that now.

By the time Siena looked back, the object had begun to move away and was much smaller. Her father returned with his binoculars, but could not spot the UFO. As Siena concluded, "This is all I saw. I don't know where it went or what happened to it from there on."

Her father had regrets, too. He wrote: "I've seen many queer objects but none so real and yet so mystifying as we saw in our field. If only I would have driven to it as I intended. Why did it take off so soon after our sighting? Did they or it see us? Why can't I forget it? If it would only come back."

Since you may only see one UFO in your entire life, make sure that you don't repeat the Pokornys' mistake. As soon as you spot a UFO, keep watching until it disappears.

2. Be aware of everything that's happening.

You may be looking at the UFO as it lands. The first thing you should ask is, "Is this a bright light or an actual object?"

If it is a light, you won't be able to see any definite structure. The edges of the light may appear fuzzy or wavering.

If it is an actual object, how do you know? What do you see that would convince people? An object can be pulsating, rotating, emitting noises, or just sitting still. Other things are happening, too, and you must try to pay attention to them. Here are some you might notice:

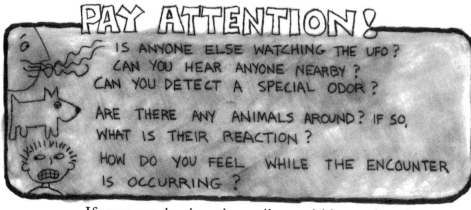

PAY ATTENTION!

IS ANYONE ELSE WATCHING THE UFO?

CAN YOU HEAR ANYONE NEARBY?

CAN YOU DETECT A SPECIAL ODOR?

ARE THERE ANY ANIMALS AROUND? IF SO, WHAT IS THEIR REACTION?

HOW DO YOU FEEL WHILE THE ENCOUNTER IS OCCURRING?

If your notebook and pencil are within reach and you can grab them without taking your eyes from the UFO, now is the time to make notes. Can you write without watching your paper? You may want to practice this ability.

Be sure to note the time the encounter begins and ends; the length of the sighting is important to UFOlogists.

3. Find another witness.

Without someone to back up your story, you may not be believed. The moment you think you're seeing a UFO, try to get someone to share the experience with you. Yell once, and hope that you've attracted someone's attention. If one good yell doesn't produce other witnesses, don't keep yelling. That will only take your mind off your primary duty: observing the UFO.

A ten-year-old boy in Regal, Minnesota, reported that a UFO had landed outside his family's home one night. He told his family and then UFO investigators that a green bald-headed creature with red eyes and pointed

138

ears tapped on his bedroom window around 10:00 P.M. As the boy went to the window, the creature jumped to the ground and entered his spaceship, which was a gray blocklike object with red and orange lights at the corners. The UFO then took off.

You might not believe this encounter as it stands, but you would be more willing to believe it if the boy had called to his mother and father, and they had all watched as the UFO flew away.

Of course, even the presence of a large number of witnesses doesn't necessarily prove that a sighting occurred. On February 4, 1977, fifteen schoolboys claimed to have seen a UFO in a field near their school in Broad Haven, Wales. Some of the boys said they saw the object at lunchtime, and that it was partially hidden behind some bushes. Some said that it disappeared from time to time. Others said that they saw a UFOccupant who had pointed ears like Mr. Spock. In all, the boys watched the UFO for twenty minutes before they went to their afternoon classes. When school was over for the day, some of them returned to see if the UFO was still

139

there. At first they didn't see it. Then it rose from behind some bushes. Moments later it disappeared.

Even though fifteen boys reported seeing the UFO, their encounter was not easily believed. First, their reports indicated that the UFO must have been on the ground in full view of many houses for over two hours — an unlikely possibility, considering that no one else reported seeing the UFO. Second, even though the boys saw the UFO as a group, they could not agree on its appearance or its occupant when interviewed separately. Finally, a similar encounter had occurred in a nearby village and had been reported in the local newspaper the day before the boys saw the Broad Haven UFO. Perhaps they had read the article or had heard their parents discussing it. All in all, the fifteen eyewitnesses did not help prove that they had seen something real.

4. Don't jump to conclusions.

Whatever you do, don't assume you're seeing a TRUFO. If you pay careful attention, you may find out later what you've really seen. It's better to observe the UFO and make guesses afterward.

An excellent observer witnessed a UFO in McHenry, Illinois, on May 23, 1983. A high school art teacher and his nine-year-old daughter were bird-watching one afternoon in an isolated game reserve when they saw a strange object rise silently above the trees and slowly move along the tree line. It seemed to rock back and forth, as if it were out of control. Both observers were certain that it was going to crash, but it steadied itself and zoomed into the distance.

The art teacher did not reach any hasty conclusions. Instead he went home and sketched what he had seen. He also reported the encounter to a nearby UFO center. As he said to one investigator, "I know what I saw, but I don't know what I saw."

No one else witnessed the strange incident that day. "I think it's something my daughter and I will share for the rest of our lives," he said. "It's a moment that no one can ever take away from us. We talk about it quite often, but we don't dwell on it."

5. Take a photograph.

If your camera is handy, quickly get ready to snap a picture.

First, make sure that your camera is loaded and that the lens cap (if it has one) is off. One of the biggest mistakes that UFO photographers make in their excitement is not being prepared. You may only have a few seconds to take your photo.

Second, try to get as much in the UFO picture as you can. Include some background or foreground. If there are mountains, trees, houses, or power lines nearby, try to show them in the picture. This will help UFOlogists decide how large your UFO was. It may also help prove that your picture is not a fake.

Third, hold your camera steady. Even if you feel calm, your hands may be shaking. If a tree or a fencepost is nearby, brace the camera against it. This is especially important if you are taking night pictures.

Fourth, take as many pictures as you can, especially if the UFO is moving. This way, your film will be more like film from a movie camera. By taking ten pictures in just a few moments' time you will help to prove that your UFO was real.

Fifth, have your film developed promptly by a photography lab that will not cut the film into strips. One problem for UFO photographers is proving that short strips of film are all from the same roll. UFOlogists want to make sure that photos have not been staged. To verify this, they want to look at the entire roll of film. If it's in sections, they can't be sure that you haven't put a number of rolls of film together. If the whole roll is available, they can detect any trickery.

Finally, keep your film in a safe place. After UFOlogists have seen a set of prints from your roll of film, they may ask you to send them the film for study. If you think that the film is irreplaceable, you may want to ask the UFOlogists to visit you.

PHOTOGRAPHY TIPS for UFOLogists

1. Camera loaded lens cap off

2. Get a lot into the picture.

3. Hold it steady.

4. Take a lot of pictures.

5. Have film developed by a lab that won't cut it into strips.

6. Keep film in a safe place.

If you're thinking of creating a fake UFO photo, you may want to consider the trouble the following case caused. On January 9, 1967, two brothers named Dan and Grant Jaroslaw, from Mount Clemens, Michigan, said they saw a UFO. Fortunately, the brothers told reporters, they had had their camera with them and were able to take four pictures of the craft. Because they were using Polaroid film, there were no negatives to study, only the four pictures.

Investigators were impressed. They were not suspicious because it would not have been possible to alter the Polaroid film in a darkroom. They also believed the brothers because the Jaroslaws did not want any publicity or money for the photos. One of the top UFOlogists, Dr. J. Allen Hynek, said of the photos: "In all honesty . . . I cannot call them a hoax." As time passed, the photos were often referred to as evidence that UFOs exist.

In 1976, however, Grant Jaroslaw wrote to Dr. Hynek admitting that the photos had been faked. Dan had made a model of a UFO and attached it to white thread tied between two poles. Grant believed that the thread would show and didn't want to waste any film on the prank; Dan talked him into trying one shot. As Grant wrote to Dr. Hynek:

> The weather conditions were just right, the photo came out so real looking that we took some more. . . . We showed our mother the photos and pretended they were real. But, before

we knew it . . . she had called the newspaper.

Dan and I . . . decided to let the paper have the story. We made it up as the reporter asked the questions. . . . We just didn't think the story would become as big as it did.

We are sorry if we caused anyone any trouble over this.

What began as a prank rapidly turned into one of the biggest UFO photography hoaxes of all time.

6. Don't lie or embellish the truth.

This is important. No matter what you see, never attempt to make it stranger or more normal than it actually was. Your only chance of being believed is to tell the truth as accurately and as sincerely as you can.

Take the case of Dwight McKenzie, who was returning to Oldham, England, one night after visiting some friends in Liverpool. Dwight was riding on his motorbike and stopped by the side of the road for a drink of tea from his Thermos. He told investigators later that he heard a humming sound in a nearby field and saw two figures silhouetted by a silver glow. The figures approached him, and Dwight, who thought they might be poachers, decided to leave.

He heard a voice say, "Don't be afraid." When he turned toward the figures again, he saw that they were a man and a woman, about five feet tall. His headlight illuminated the area, and he could see that both had blond hair and seemed to be wearing belted ski suits. Each belt had an egg-shaped object where the buckle should be.

145

"Where did you come from?" Dwight asked.

"From the third solar system," the woman said.

"Why are you here?" Dwight asked, thinking that he should pinch himself to see if he was dreaming.

"We have to make some minor adjustments to our craft," she replied.

They talked for a few more minutes. Then the man and the woman walked away, and Dwight watched as a cigar-shaped UFO took off "at a speed you wouldn't believe."

146

Two months after the encounter, Dwight contacted a local UFO organization with his account. After some investigation, including a check with Dwight's friends, the UFO group concluded that Dwight was lying about the incident. His friends had told the investigators that he was a notorious liar and offered examples of the type of tale he was known to make up.

The moral of this story is, if you want to be believed, make sure you have a history of telling the truth.

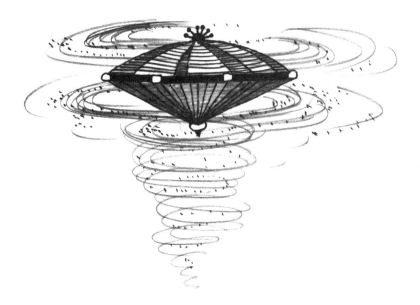

10. Writing a UFO Report

When your UFO encounter ends, you have quick work to do. Unless you can still see the UFO in the distance, you should not run home or call the police. What you should do is find a quiet spot and fill out your *UFO report*.

Many different kinds of UFO report forms exist. Almost every UFO organization has its own. Here's one that I've compiled, using a number of current forms.

ENCOUNTER INFORMATION

Date of encounter _____ Time encounter began _____

Time encounter ended _____

Location _____

PART I Check as many as apply.

WERE YOU: ☐ indoors ☐ in a car ☐ in an airplane
☐ on a bicycle ☐ at playground ☐ taking a picture
☐ looking through a window ☐ wearing glasses
☐ using binoculars or telescope

WAS THE AREA: ☐ country ☐ city ☐ residential

WHAT WAS NEARBY: ☐ power lines ☐ airport
☐ railroad ☐ lake or reservoir ☐ houses
☐ woods ☐ river ☐ mountains ☐ other:

WAS THE WEATHER: ☐ clear ☐ partly cloudy
☐ foggy ☐ overcast ☐ rainy ☐ snowy ☐ windy

WHAT ELSE YOU SAW: ☐ moon ☐ sun
☐ stars ☐ airplane ☐ balloon ☐ meteor
☐ other:

PART II Answer the following questions completely on a separate sheet:

1. Describe the object you saw.

2. What did the object do?

3. Did any strange things occur during your experience? If so, what were they?

4. Draw a picture or a diagram of the object. If you saw anyone leave or enter the object, draw a picture of that person.

WITNESS INFORMATION

WITNESS NAME _____

Address: _____

Birthdate _____ Highest year in school _____

Occupation: _____

Have you ever had any similar encounters? If so, please explain.

How were you feeling before your encounter? Were you taking any medication?

What was your reaction during the encounter? How did you feel?

Did you notice any side effects after your encounter? If so, what?

Have you read much about UFOs or seen many movies about them?

Check One:

☐ You may use my name in reports.

☐ You may NOT use my name in reports.

Signed: _____

Date

Make sure you fill out the report immediately, while the encounter is still fresh in your memory.

Give the date and time of the encounter. The time and duration of the encounter are especially important. Many people never look at their watches to note how long their encounter lasted. Guesses about the length of time something takes are usually incorrect.

Describe the location as specifically as you can. Where did the encounter take place? What are the nearest roads or landmarks? Try to describe the location clearly enough so that someone unfamiliar with your area could find the site of your encounter.

Check every box that applies to your encounter. UFOlogists will want to know where you were at the time of the encounter and whether you were looking through any kind of optical device, even a window. Some people have claimed to see UFOs when in fact they saw reflections in their glasses or telescope — or dirt on a windowpane.

Investigators want to know what kind of area the encounter took place in and any special features. UFOs may be attracted to certain kinds of locations, so take a good look at the site of your encounter.

They will also want to know about the weather at the time and what other celestial objects you might have seen. Some people have mistaken the moon or the planet Venus for a UFO. If your encounter took place on a clear night when a full moon should have been in view, and you claim to have seen a UFO that looked like a large circle of white light, and you say that you did not see the moon, your encounter will not be taken very seriously.

Describe what you saw. Here you must give as much detail as you possibly can.

- *Size.* Determining size is difficult to do, except in comparison to other objects. Picture the sizes of the full moon and a twinkling star. How large was the object in comparison to the moon and the star?

- *Distance.* How far away was it? Try to give the distance in terms of other objects at the site. Was it hovering over a cluster of trees? Was it circling a house in the distance? Did it cast a shadow or a beam of light on a certain area or object? If you give the approximate size and the distance, UFOlogists and their computers will be able to determine how large the object actually was.

- *Shape.* Forget about the shapes you've studied in this book. Exactly what shape did your UFO have? Although it might have looked like a flying football or saucer, it might have had an irregular shape instead. Describe it completely.

- *Structure.* What did the object seem to be made of? Did you detect any metallic parts? Or did it seem to be made of cloth? Did it have a quilted surface? Could you see any seams or bolts, as you might on an airplane, or was it smooth? Did you see any portholes or windows? Did it have a dome? If so, was the dome made of the same material as the rest of the object? Finally, did it appear solid, or was it transparent?

- *Color.* What color was it? Did it appear to change color? If so, could its color have been a reflection on a metallic surface? Did it appear shiny or dull? Did it glow or have lights stationed on it? Did the glow seem like a ceiling light (coming from within) or like a car's headlights (directed away from the object)? If you noticed lights on the top and bottom, how many were there and what colors were they?

To make your descriptions as accurate as possible, you may want to use a color chart, like those available from paint stores, to identify the colors you saw. Make sure you attach the chart to your report.

Describe what the object did.

- *Movements.* Which direction did the object come from (if it was moving)? Did it change its movements during the encounter?

Refer to this list for some help in describing the movements you saw:

change direction   zoom
fall like a leaf   pulsate
spin   turn sharply
descend / ascend   hover
do aerial acrobatics   wobble

● *Special features.* Did your UFO display any special features? For example, did it leave a trail of vapor or light? Did it change shape? Did anything or anyone enter or leave the object? Did the UFO make any sounds or give off any odors? Were you aware of any heat? Did it leave anything behind?

● *Activities.* Did the object perform any of the following activities?

chase a person
follow a bicycle
follow a car
land on the water
land on the ground
discharge occupants
take on occupants
stop for repairs
cast a light beam
disappear

WHAT DID IT DO

Give as many details as you can about these activities. For example, if it cast a light beam, what color was the light? Where was the light directed? Was anything illuminated?

- *UFOccupants.* Describe any beings you saw and their position. Were they inside or outside the UFO? If inside, did you see them through a window or door? If outside, did you see them leave the craft? Make sure you indicate how far the UFOccupant was from your location.

Next, describe the UFOccupant. Begin with the head: its covering (if any); the shape, number, and color of its eyes; its nose, mouth, and hair (if any); the color and texture of its skin. Then describe the body. How tall was it? Did it have arms and legs? Did it have hands or claws? Did it glow?

What was the UFOccupant wearing? Did its clothes seem manmade? Were they like a skin-diving suit or a pair of overalls? Was the being wearing gloves, shoes, or boots?

What was the UFOccupant doing? Did it walk or float? Did it disappear into thin air? Did it have any weapons or tools? If there was more than one occupant, did they talk to each other? If so, did their lips move? Did they gesture? Could you hear them speak? What did they sound like?

- *Effects on machinery.* Note whether the UFO seemed to interfere with the performance of any nearby machines. If you were in an automobile, were the engine, headlights, radio, or other electrical components affected? Did your watch stop?

Here's a checklist of items that might be affected:

- ☐ house lights
- ☐ hearing aid
- ☐ television
- ☐ fuses
- ☐ watches/clocks

- ☐ streetlights
- ☐ telephone
- ☐ circuit breakers
- ☐ compass
- ☐ radio

- *Effects on humans.* Was your behavior affected in any way? Could you move, or were you temporarily paralyzed? Were you calm and curious, or did you feel fearful? Did you sense that you were being watched?

- *Effects on animals.* Were any pets or other animals disturbed by the object? Animals do not imagine seeing things; if an animal is truly disturbed, something is likely to be really happening. Remember, though, that animals can be frightened by a low-flying airplane. You may want to use the following list to indicate how the animal was bothered:

- ☐ barked
- ☐ started
- ☐ hid
- ☐ shook
- ☐ kicked

- ☐ whined
- ☐ panicked
- ☐ disobeyed
- ☐ paced
- ☐ covered ears

Afterward, you should consider the following questions. Did the pet have a poor appetite? Was it disobedient? Did it refuse to return to the scene of the encounter? If the UFO landed near a chicken coop or cow barn, pay attention to the number of eggs the hens laid later on or the amount of milk produced by the cows. Was there a change? You may not know about the effects of the encounter for a few days, so you will have to include more details later.

Describe any strange parts of the experience. Seeing a distant flying light or shape is not particularly unusual, but if the light moves in unexpected ways and changes direction rapidly, the encounter becomes strange. If the light lands nearby and discharges UFOccupants, it qualifies as a highly strange encounter.

Think of strange encounters and UFOccupants on a scale such as the following.

158

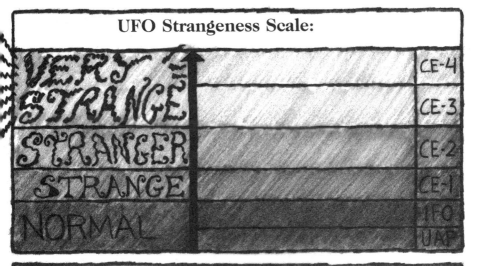

UFO Strangeness Scale:

VERY		CE-4
STRANGE		CE-3
STRANGER		CE-2
STRANGE		CE-1
NORMAL		IFO
		UAP

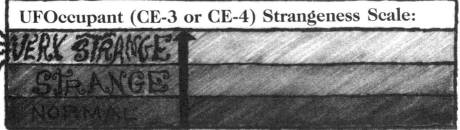

UFOccupant (CE-3 or CE-4) Strangeness Scale:

VERY STRANGE	
STRANGE	
NORMAL	

The closer your UFO is to the top of the scale, the stranger the encounter is. The stranger your aliens are, the more likely it is they come from a TRUFO. For example, if you see a normal-looking man repairing a helicopter-type object in the middle of the Mojave Desert, you are near the bottom of the Strangeness Scale. But if you see two dwarflike aliens with yellow skin and green eyes in the shape of pumpkin seeds emerge from a glowing orb of white light and fly toward you, you're much closer to the top.

159

Draw a picture of the object and any UFOccupants. You don't have to be an artist to sketch your object. Just pick up a pencil and a sheet of paper and draw away. You may want to make notes to clarify something that's hard to draw (such as the expression on a UFOccupant's face).

Once you've described your experience thoroughly, you need to give some details about yourself.

List personal information.

This includes your name, address, birthdate, year in school, and/or your occupation.

Discuss any similar experiences you've had.

Have you seen UFOs before? If so, you should include this fact in the report. If you omit it and a UFOlogist finds out that you have, he or she will be much less likely to believe your report.

160

If you have seen another UFO, describe when it happened and what you saw. If you filled out a UFO report form about it, attach a copy of that report. If you've seen a number of UFOs, you're not likely to be believed at all. Most people go through their lives without witnessing even one. If you claim to have seen half a dozen over a period of time, a UFOlogist may suspect that you're turning every passing airplane into a UFO. In that case, you'll need to become a better observer and jump to fewer conclusions.

Describe how you were feeling before you saw the UFO. Some UFOlogists think that a person's mood may be related to his or her ability to see a UFO. If you were upset or angry, happy or sad, thoughtful or zany, include this in your report.

If you were feeling ill and had taken an aspirin or any other medicine, make sure you report this. The medicine could have affected your powers of observation.

Describe how you felt during the encounter. People who have seen UFOs often report a kind of *Wizard of Oz* response, according to UFOlogist Jenny Randles. If you've watched that movie, you will remember how Dorothy felt when she arrived in Munchkinland. "I have a feeling we're not in Kansas anymore, Toto," she says in a calm but confused voice. Her reaction is similar to that of UFObservers. First, they do not feel afraid of whatever's happening. Second, they feel as if only they and the UFO exist. It's almost as if everything else in

161

the world has disappeared. Finally, they lose all sense of time and are nearly hypnotized by the strange occurrence.

Describe any side effects that you noticed afterward. Most people who see UFOs experience no side effects whatsoever. However, here are some you might look for:

METALLIC TASTE	STINGING EYES
SUNBURNED SKIN	SORE EARS
DIZZINESS	HEADACHE
NIGHTMARES	MUSCLE ACHES

Finally, list the books you've read or movies you've seen that deal with UFOs. A UFOlogist will want to know whether you have an active interest in UFOs. If you've seen *E.T.* twenty times and read every UFO book in your school library, your interest may count against you. Remember: the more you think about UFOs, the more you'll expect to see one. The more you read about UFOs, the more knowledgeable you'll become.

If you see one, you will be asked if you've seen many UFO movies, read many UFO books, and thought about UFOs very much. If you answer yes to any or all of these questions, you'll be labeled as someone with "UFOs on the brain," and you may no longer be the best witness to your own experience, since your beliefs may cloud your thinking. Are you sure you weren't seeing an airplane? Are you sure that the alien creature wasn't just a person in a jumpsuit?

If you are an avid UFO fan, the UFOlogist may still believe you, as long as he or she accepts that you did not imagine your UFO. This is why you should never jump to conclusions. Be as objective and as scientific as possible.

When you've seen a UFO and confessed that you have read a lot about UFOs, how can you make sure that you are taken seriously?

Avoid all publicity after a sighting. If you call the *National Enquirer* to report your story, hoping to be paid, people will discredit your encounter. Anyone can make up a UFO story for money. A person who really sees one will seek to stay in the background.

Even calling your local newspaper can be a mistake. Many people have done just that, only to be ridiculed. Ask yourself, "What do I hope to gain if the newspaper prints a story about my encounter?"

Inform the proper authorities. To whom should you report your UFO? The air force? The Department of Defense? Many UFOlogists believe that the air force and the Defense Department are no longer interested in

UFO reports. This leaves you with just two possibilities: the police and a UFO organization. You may want to report your UFO to your local police department simply to find out whether anyone else saw a UFO when you did. Unless the UFO is still on view, however, the police may not take your call seriously. After all, what can they do about a UFO that has already disappeared?

Perhaps the best place is a UFO organization. Many of these exist. Unfortunately, some last for only a few years and then close. One of the most respected is the Center for UFO Studies (CUFOS), which is located at 2457 W. Peterson Avenue, Chicago, Illinois 60659. After your UFO report is completed, you will probably want to send CUFOS a copy for its files and perhaps, if your experience had a high degree of strangeness, further investigation.

If your sighting is too amazing to wait, however, CUFOS has a twenty-four-hour telephone number: (312) 271-3611. You can leave a message, along with your address and telephone number. Someone at CUFOS will contact you, either by mail or by phone.

Another organization is the Mutual UFO Network (MUFON) located at 103 Oldtowne Road, Seguin, Texas 78155.

All this should come in handy if you have a close encounter. But you may decide to become a UFOlogist and specialize in studying the UFOs that other people have seen. You might ask, "Don't UFOlogists see

164

UFOs?" In fact, most of the UFOlogists I've met have never seen a UFO, although some claim to have seen one when they were young, which made them decide to become UFO investigators as adults. In any event, most UFOlogists are content to study what others have seen and interview witnesses afterward.

Chapter 11 will show you how.

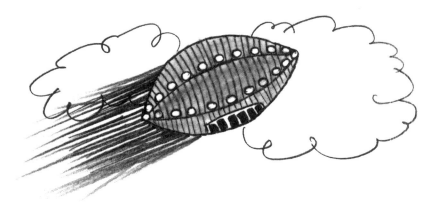

11. Using Your UFO Kit

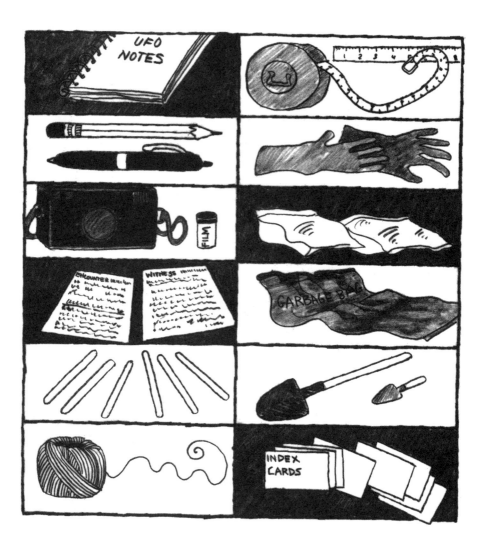

Before you can conduct any investigations, you'll need a UFO hunter's kit. You know that your kit should contain a notebook, a pen or pencil, a camera, and UFO report forms. To become a UFOlogist, you must add other equipment that could help you prove there has been a close encounter. In fact, you may want to carry this special UFO kit with you, so that it is always handy in case any unexpected company drops in.

Your kit should contain the following items.

notebook	tape measure
pen or pencil	rubber gloves
camera and film	small plastic bags
UFO report forms	large garbage bags
Popsicle sticks	garden spade
string	ruler
	index cards

Your kit will be most useful after a CE-2 or CE-3, when traces of a landing are apparent. You can use it after you've seen a UFO land and then zoom away. You can also use it to investigate the landing of a UFO you did not observe.

Imagine that a friend calls you in a panic one day. She saw a UFO fly over her house. A little later she noticed a burned area in a field behind her house. Since she knows that you have studied UFOlogy, she suggests that you investigate the field. Perhaps the UFO landed there.

What should you do?

Grab your UFO kit and hurry to the site, before anyone else has a chance to disturb it. You will probably want to take along a friend or a parent to help you. If the site is on private property, be sure to get permission from the owner. Then follow these steps.

1. Inspect the site from the sidelines.

Record its location and appearance in your *notebook*. Remember: be sure to stay on the edges of the site to start with. You don't want to walk on any evidence.

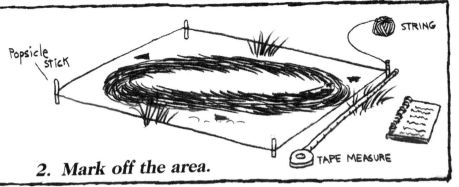

2. Mark off the area.

To do this, determine where the landing site ends. Place
Popsicle sticks or other small wooden stakes at the four
corners of the site, then rope off the area with *string*.
Try to make an even rectangle. Once you have finished,
measure each length of string with your *tape measure* to
determine the size of the area, and record it in your
notebook.

3. Make a grid of the site.

Every three feet on your string marker, tie another
string. Walking outside the landing site, tie that string
to the opposite string at the same three-foot interval. In
this way you will make a kind of string grid that will
help you record what you find.

169

4. Inspect the ground inside the string boundary.

Walk through each square of the grid, taking care not to step on anything that looks like physical evidence of a landing.

Ask yourself the following questions:

- What does the earth look like? Is it burned, scratched, or scorched? Is there a crater? Are any patches dug up? Do you see any indentations or depressions?
- If you find a large depression in the earth, what shape is it? It may have been made by the UFO when it landed. Is it triangular, oval, rectangular? Or does it have a jagged shape?
- Do you see any footprints? If so, do they look like human footprints? Are they of bare feet or shoes? If the footprints are of bare feet, make sure you count the number of toes and record this information. If the footprints appear to have been made by shoes, look for any signs that they were manufactured on Earth. Are there any special tread marks or designs? Note these as well. You will want to photograph any interesting physical evidence, so you should try to take a clear photo of any footprints.
- Is there any debris that the UFO might have left behind? This could include strange-looking pieces of metal or rock, charred earth, discolored grass or plants, suspicious liquid. If you see something mechanical, stop

and report your find to the local police. You may need help. Be sure not to touch anything you see. Leave this item alone until you finish walking through the grid.

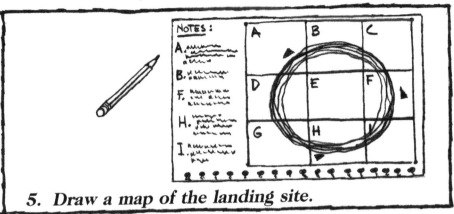

5. Draw a map of the landing site.

Prepare a sheet of paper in your notebook with the same number of boxes as your string grid. With this paper, walk back through the grid, following the same path. This time, indicate on your paper where each strange area or object is located, using the grid to guide you.

Assign each box a letter of the alphabet (if your grid has more than twenty-six squares, continue with AA, BB, CC, and so on). Then quickly sketch what you have found in that box of the grid. If you've found some charred earth and a small piece of metal in Box A, your sketch might look like this:

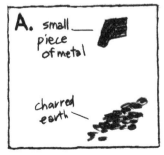

When you're done, you will have a complete sketch of the entire landing site.

6. Preserve all physical evidence.

Once you've drawn your map using the grid, you're ready to do a closer inspection. For this, you'll need *rubber gloves*, some *small plastic bags*, perhaps some *large plastic garbage bags*, a *spade*, a *camera*, a *ruler*, and *index cards* or other writing material to tag your samples.

Again, go through the grid using the same path. If all of the evidence seems safe to touch, approach the first piece. Wearing your rubber gloves, pick it up carefully. Inspect it, then describe it and its location on an index card. Give each item a number as well. An index card might look like this:

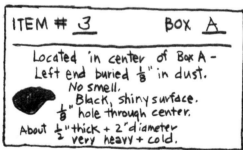

```
ITEM # 3              BOX A
─────────────────────────────
    Located in center of Box A -
    Left end buried ⅛" in dust.
         No smell.
        Black, shiny surface.
      ⅛" hole through center.
  About ½"thick + 2"diameter
         very heavy + cold.
```

Next, place your ruler beside the item to indicate its size and snap a photograph. This kind of photograph is useful to other investigators or in case your evidence

172

disappears. Put each piece of evidence into a separate plastic bag. Finally, tie the index card tightly onto the bag and store the bag in a safe place.

If you come across unusual soil, dig up a few scoops with your spade. Put each scoop into a separate bag and mark the sample's location on your map and the index card.

7. Draw a map of the general area.

Once you've cataloged the evidence in the landing site and have completed your string grid map, you will need to draw a map of the entire area. This should be done on a larger scale.

Include the closest roads, buildings, woods, or lakes. Mark the site of the landing and, if known, the direction the UFO arrived from and left toward. If there was a witness to the encounter, also indicate where the witness was located.

A completed map might look like this:

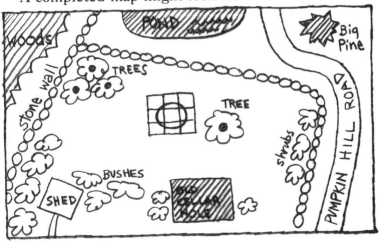

8. Interview your friend and any other witnesses.

You'll need a tape recorder — and your friend's permission to record the interview. Remember that anyone who has seen a UFO may be a bit upset or confused. You will want to respect her right to privacy. You will also want to assure the witness that the interview will be kept confidential if she desires.

First, talk to your friend informally. Don't talk about "flying saucers." If you're interviewing a witness you don't already know, get to know the person and allow him or her to become acquainted with you.

Once you have permission for the interview, it is wise to take a companion, if possible, and a list of prepared questions. Before the interview, ask the witness to complete the UFO report form. Once he or she has done that, you should look it over and then proceed with your questions. Your goals are to uncover as much information as you can and to make sure that the witness is telling the truth.

Although every investigation is different, you may want to ask the following questions:

What did you see, from start to finish?
Did you ever look away during the encounter? If so, why?
Describe the object completely. Were there any lights on it? What color were they?

Was it similar to anything you've seen before?

Did you see anyone in the same area? If so, do you know who it was? Did you see anyone enter or leave the object?

Did you lose any time from the start of the encounter to its conclusion? Does your watch have the correct time now?

Have you seen any UFOs before?

9. Compare all witness reports of the same UFO.

For example, if you find two other people who claim to have seen the same UFO as your friend, you should compare their stories. Interview only one person at a time, and make sure that no one can overhear the other witnesses. The more the witnesses agree about the UFO, the more believable their story is. But if they've talked to one another before you interview them, you might wonder if they made their stories up. The best witnesses are those who do not know each other and who were unaware that anyone else saw the UFOs.

As you can see, becoming a tried-and-TRUFO UFOlogist is not an easy job. But with patience and energy, you can learn to conduct a serious investigation. In fact, you may want to set up a grid in your own back yard for practice.

12. Becoming a UFOlogist

On a Monday night in September some years ago, a
teenage boy named Rick was in his back yard in Columbus, Ohio, putting some hay in his rabbit's pen. It was
dark as he completed his chore. Since this was a heavily
wooded neighborhood, without streetlights, the only
light came from his family's house.

Then he heard a strange clapping sound.

Here is what Rick said happened next: "I turned
and . . . a creature! It was walking into the woods! It
was dressed in a black uniform with a silver belt. Its
arms and legs moved in rhythm. But its head! It glowed
with an eerie yellow glow. It was large and the shadows
of the tree branches put dark streaks through the head."

Rick knew he should try to follow the creature as it
walked toward the woods. After all, it had not even noticed him. Instead he ran to the house and screamed for

his parents. When he explained what had happened, his family jumped into the car and drove around the area looking for the creature. They found nothing. Rick's parents told him that someone had probably dressed up to scare him and to keep the story a secret.

The next morning a neighbor asked Rick's mother if they had seen strange lights in a nearby field the night before. The family went to the field and found a large oval area where the vegetation had been flattened. Even though Rick's parents believed him, they warned him to keep quiet, since people might consider him "nuts."

For almost sixteen years, Rick did just that, until he saw an advertisement in the Columbus *Dispatch* seeking people who had observed UFOs. Rick responded.

Now that so much time had passed, Rick's memory of the incident was weak. Still, when he was interviewed by Irena Scott, a physiologist at the Ohio State University Medical School who was interested in the subject of UFOs, he remembered that the creature was too tall and thin to be a human being. He also remembered that its head was oval and lit up like a neon light. The head seemed transparent, which is why Rick had originally described the creature as having no brain. He clearly remembered that it wore a metallic belt that seemed to have an instrument panel. The neighbor who saw the strange lights in the field was also interviewed, but remembered very little. After sixteen years, it's not surprising.

Many people think that anyone who sees a UFO is a crackpot or unstable. Rick, who had completed his bachelor's degree at Ohio State and was finishing his master's degree when he replied to the advertisement, had seen something on that September night. Whether it was an alien from a UFO is another matter, though — one that might have been solved if Rick had reported the encounter when it happened.

Rick told Dr. Scott: "I wish I could offer more detail. . . . Many, many times I've gazed up at the heavens . . . and wondered what it was that I saw . . . so many years ago."

If Rick had been a UFOlogist when he was younger, his story might have had a conclusive ending. If he had investigated his sighting or even reported it, he might have learned what he saw that night. Maybe it was just a trickster; maybe it was a jogger in a reflective suit. Or maybe it was a UFOccupant.

A similar experience happened to fourteen-year-old Peter Hough in Cheshire, England. One morning in October 1968, Peter was delivering newspapers when he saw what he thought was a model airplane caught in a nearby tree. He looked at the object for a moment. As he did, he realized that it was not caught in the branches but was hovering in the sky behind the tree. The object was tilted at an angle. Slowly it leveled itself and began to move.

Peter wrote later:

> For a moment it was hidden by a tree, and when I next saw it, it was (as far as I could judge) some 100 feet . . . higher in the sky.
>
> At this point, two things became clear. The craft was about half a mile away . . . and the physical appearance became clearer. To put it bluntly, the craft resembled a crude cross, the sort of thing a boy may carve with a knife from an old scrap of wood. It was not in the least streamlined, both ends were blunt, and the wings came out at right angles.

Peter watched the craft for some five minutes altogether. During this time it moved slowly, then appeared to remain stationary. Finally it began to move again, completed a semicircular route, then made a sharp right-angled turn before cruising out of sight.

Although Peter, like Rick, did not report his UFO, he spent the next two years wondering what it could have been. At last, in September 1970, he wrote a six-page report on the sighting and included a sketch of the object and various maps locating the encounter. What's more, this experience led to Peter's decision to become a UFOlogist. Now the chairman of a local UFO organization in England, Peter has investigated hundreds of UFO sightings and has written books and articles on the subject. His interest in the subject began on that October morning when he saw something he couldn't explain.

180

Now that you've finished this book, you know more about UFOs than Rick or Peter knew when they were young. As you watch the sky, waiting to see a UFO, what will you do if you see bright lights approaching? Will you turn away? Will you run to tell someone else? Or will you have the courage to face the unknown and explore it? And will you accept the reality of whatever you see, TRUFO or not?

Your answer to this question is the final test of a true UFOlogist.

Acknowledgments

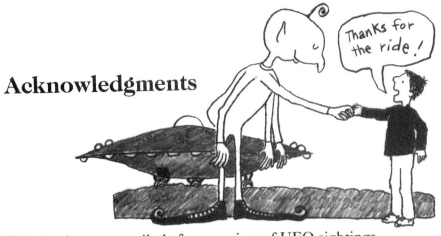

This book was compiled after a review of UFO sightings reported over the past forty years or so. I would particularly like to thank the Center for UFO Studies (CUFOS) in Chicago and the Manchester (England) UFO Research Association for providing access to their files of sightings, to the Anomalous Phenomenon Review Association for UFOIN case files, and to the Newcastle-upon-Tyne (England) Central Library for the use of its wide-ranging collection of UFO material. I am grateful to George Eberhart and Mark Rodeghier of CUFOS, to Peter Hough and Jenny Randles of MUFORA, to Robert Morrell and Syd Henley of APRA, and to Moira Gray and June Leach of the Newcastle Library (and Tourist Information Center) for answering my questions and providing leads to valuable material.

Although I have used many documents in the preparation of this book, the materials in the following list have been the most valuable. Although most of these were written for adults, a few are suitable for younger readers. These are marked with an asterisk (*).

Bibliography

Andrews, Colin. "The Lost Harrier Jet and the Cornfield Rings." *Flying Saucer Review* 33 (June 1988), 7–13.

Arvey, Michael. *UFOs*. San Diego: Greenhaven Press, 1989.

Baker, Gray. *The Silver Bridge*. Clarksburg, West Virginia: Saucerian Books, 1970.

Berger, Melvin. *UFOs, ETs, & Visitors from Outer Space*. New York: Putnam, 1988.

*Bloecher, Ted. "CE-III Report from Montvale, N.J.: Preliminary Report. *The MUFON UFO Journal* 123 (February 1978), 4–7.

Blundell, Nigel, and Roger Boar. *The World's Greatest UFO Mysteries*. London: Octopus Books, 1989.

Bord, Janet and Colin. *Modern Mysteries of Britain*. London: Grafton, 1988.

Bowen, Charles, ed. *The Humanoids*. London: Futura, 1974.

Branley, Franklyn M. *A Book of Flying Saucers for You*. New York: Crowell, 1973.

Brookesmith, Peter, ed. *The UFO Casebook*. London: Orbis, 1984.

Butler, Brenda, Dot Street, and Jenny Randles. *Sky Crash*. London: Grafton, 1986.

Cassirer, Manfred. *Parapsychology and the UFO*. London: M. Cassirer, 1988.

Clark, Jerome, and Lucius Farish. "The 1897 Story." *Flying Saucer Review* 14 (November/December 1968), 6–7.

Cohen, Daniel. *A Close Look at Close Encounters*. New York: Dodd Mead, 1981.

———. *The Great Airship Mystery: A UFO of the 1890s*. New York: Dodd Mead, 1981.

*Delgado, Pat, and Colin Andrews. *Circular Evidence*. London: Bloomsbury, 1989.

Devereux, Paul. *Earth Lights Revelation*. London: Blandford, 1989.

Emenegger, Robert. *UFOs, Past, Present, and Future*. New York: Ballantine, 1974.

Evans, Hilary. "Dyfed Enigma." In Peter Brookesmith, ed., *The Alien World*. London: Orbis, 1984.

———, and John Spencer, eds. *UFOs 1947–1987: The 40-Year Search for an Explanation*. London: Fortean Tomes, 1987.

Fawcett, Lawrence, and Barry J. Greenwood. *Clear Intent: The Government Coverup of the UFO Experience*. Englewood Cliffs, N.J.: Prentice Hall, 1984.

Fowler, Raymond E. *Casebook of a UFO Investigator*. Englewood Cliffs, N.J.: Prentice Hall, 1981.

———, ed. *MUFON Field Investigator's Manual*. Seguin, Tex.: Mutual UFO Network, 1983.

———. *UFOs: Interplanetary Visitors*. Englewood Cliffs, N.J.: Prentice Hall, 1974.

Fuller, Paul. "Mystery Circles: Myth in the Making." *International UFO Reporter* 13 (May/June 1988), 4–8.

Furniss, Tim. *Aliens*. London: Granada, 1984.

Good, Timothy, ed. *The UFO Report 1990*. London: Sidgwick and Jackson, 1989.

Haines, Richard R. *Observing UFOs*. Chicago: Nelson-Hall, 1980.

Hall, Richard. *Uninvited Guests*. Santa Fe, N.M.: Aurora, 1988.

Hansen, Kim. "UFO Casebook (13 Case Histories)." In Evans and Spencer, *UFOs 1947–1987*, pp. 48–92.

*Hendry, Allan. *The UFO Handbook*. Garden City, N.Y.: Doubleday, 1979.

Hopkins, Budd. "CE-III Account from Montvale, N.J.: Final Report on a High-Strangeness Case, Incorporating Material from Ted Bloecher's Preliminary Report." Unpublished report.

Hough, Peter. "Ufo Occupants." In Evans and Spencer, *UFOs 1947–1987*, pp. 126–31.

*Hynek, Allen J., and Philip J. Imbrogno, with Bob Pratt. *Night Siege: The Hudson Valley Sightings*. New York: Ballantine, 1987.

Jamison, Benton. "A Fire in the Forest: New Light on the Rendlesham Landing." *International UFO Reporter* 13 (September/October 1988), 4–17, 21.

Keatman, Martin, and Stephen Banks. "More Children and UFOs." *Flying Saucer Review* 26 (November 1980), 18–21.

———. "Report on Two UFO Cases." Unpublished report. UFOIN File #7746.

Keel, John A. "The People Problem." In Spencer and Evans, *Phenomenon*, pp. 186–98.

———. "West Virginia's Enigmatic 'Bird.' " *Flying Saucer Review* 14 (July/August 1968), 7–14.

Keul, Alex, and Ken Phillips. "Assessing the Witness." In Evans and Spencer, *UFOs 1947–1987*, pp. 230–37.

*Larson, Sherman J. *Close Encounters: A Factual Report on UFOs.* Milwaukee: Raintree, 1978.

Maccabee, Bruce, "The Fantastic Flight of JAL 1628." *International UFO Reporter* 12 (March/April 1987), 4–23.

Mayer, Ann Margaret. *Who's Out There: UFO Encounters.* New York: Messner, 1979.

McCampbell, James M. *UFOlogy.* Millbrae, Calif.: Celestial Arts, 1976.

Mosbleck, Gerald. "The Elusive Photographic Evidence." In Spencer and Evans, *Phenomenon*, pp. 208–11.

Phillips, Ted R. "Close Encounters of the Second Kind: Physical Traces." In Walter H. Andrus, Jr., and Dennis W. Stacy, eds., *UFOs: The Hidden Evidence.* Proceedings of the 12th Annual MUFON UFO Symposium, Massachusetts Institute of Technology, July 25–26, 1981. Seguin, Tex.: Mutual UFO Network, 1981.

Pugh, Randall Jones. "Broad Haven School Report." *Flying Saucer Review* 23 (June 1977), 3–5.

———, and F. W. Holiday. *The Dyfed Enigma.* London: Coronet, 1981.

Randles, Jenny, *Abduction.* London: Robert Hale, 1988.

———. *The Pennine UFO Mystery.* London: Granada, 1983.

———. *UFO Reality: A Critical Look at the Physical Evidence.* London: Robert Hale, 1983.

———. *UFO Study: A Handbook for Enthusiasts.* London: Robert Hale, 1981.

———, and Peter Warrington. *Science and the UFOs.* New York: Basil Blackwell, 1987.

———, and Paul Whetnall. "Four Young Men and a UFO." *Flying Saucer Review* 26 (September 1980), 5–7.

Rimmer, John. *The Evidence for Alien Abductions.* Wellingborough, England: Aquarian Press, 1984.

Rodeghier, Mark. *UFO Reports Involving Vehicle Interference.* Evanston, Ill.: Center for UFO Studies, 1981.

Sachs, Margaret. *The UFO Encyclopedia*. London: Corgi, 1981.

———, with Ernest Jahn. *Celestial Passengers*. New York: Penguin, 1978.

Schmitt, Don. "The Belleville Sightings: Part One." *International UFO Reporter* 12 (November/December 1987), 4–8.

———. "The Belleville Sightings: Part Two." *International UFO Reporter* 13 (January/February 1988), 17–19.

Schwartz, Berthold Eric. *UFO-Dynamics*. Books I and II. Moore Haven, Fla.: Rainbow Books, 1983.

Scott, I. "Bedroom light." *International UFO Reporter* 13 (March/April 1988), 14–15.

———. "Observation of an Alien Figure." *International UFO Reporter* 12 (January/February 1987), 20, 25.

Shaw, John. "Is a Picture Worth a Thousand Words?" In Spencer and Evans, *Phenomenon*, pp. 212–23.

Smith, Willy. "UFOs in Latin America." In Evans and Spencer, *UFOs 1947–1987*, pp. 97–113.

Spencer, John, and Hilary Evans, eds. *Phenomenon*. London: Futura, 1988.

Story, Ronald D. *Sightings*. New York: Quill, 1982.

Timmerman, John P. "A Giant Triangle." *International UFO Reporter* 11 (July/August 1986), 9–10, 22.

Vallee, Jacques. *Dimensions: A Casebook of Alien Contact*. New York: Ballantine, 1989.

Webb, Walter N. "Encounter at Buff Ledge: A UFO Case History." In Walter H. Andrus, Jr., and Richard H. Hall, eds., *Abductions and the E.T. Hypothesis*. Proceedings of the 19th Annual MUFON UFO Symposium, University of Nebraska, June 24–26, 1988. Seguin, Tex.: Mutual UFO Network, 1988.

———. "Explosive Ball Lightning." *The MUFON UFO Journal* 225 (January 1987), 12–13.

Zeidman, Jennie. "Green Light Over Mansfield." *International UFO Reporter* 13 (November/December 1988), 13–14.

———. *A Helicopter-UFO Encounter Over Ohio*. Evanston, Ill.: Center for UFO Studies, 1979.

Glossary

UFO   Unidentified flying object: any unfamiliar object that is seen in the sky or that appears to have landed.

IFO   Identified flying object: a UFO that has been identified. Perhaps someone sees a "flying saucer" in the sky, only to learn later that it was really a weather balloon. That UFO has become an IFO.

UAP   Unidentified atmospheric phenomenon: a UFO caused by a natural phenomenon, such as ball lightning or an electromagnetic field. These are natural occurrences that scientists still do not understand completely.

TRUFO	True UFO: a UFO that has been investigated and cannot be identified as either a manmade object (IFO) or a natural phenomenon (UAP). This does not mean that it comes from outer space, however.
CE-1	Close Encounter of the First Kind: a sighting of a UFO at close range.
CE-2	Close Encounter of the Second Kind: a close-range sighting of a UFO after which physical evidence of the UFO is found. 
CE-3	Close Encounter of the Third Kind: a close-range sighting of beings in or around a UFO.
CE-4	Close Encounter of the Fourth Kind: a close-range sighting of a UFO that results in the reported kidnapping of a human being for a period of time. In such cases, the human is usually subjected to examination by UFO beings.

Index